UNDERSTANDING
HEREDITY

An Introduction to Genetics

UNDERSTANDING
HEREDITY

An Introduction to Genetics

RICHARD B. GOLDSCHMIDT

University of California

NEW YORK · JOHN WILEY & SONS, INC.

LONDON · CHAPMAN & HALL, LIMITED

Preface

Genetics has attained such a central position in science that the number of students, and also laymen, who want to acquire an elementary knowledge of this subject is constantly increasing. There are a number of good—and also of not so good—books available for a scientific study of genetics on different levels. But for a large number of students who do not intend to specialize in biology, these books are too advanced and contain too much specialized material. Thus, there might be a need for a short and easily readable survey of the basic facts of genetics, which will enable also the non-biologist to grasp with only little effort the essentials of that fascinating science. It is obvious that in presenting such an introduction, the major task is to decide not what material to include but rather what material to omit. The professional geneticist will notice on almost every page the omission of facts and interpretations dear to him. But such restrictions make the essentials clear and convincing and make the facts easily accessible to the beginner, permitting him to see the great outlines of our science not blurred by unending details. The best success this little book could attain would be to make its student desirous of attacking one of the more advanced treatises.

At the present time there is not only a great desire for information on genetics noticeable among all classes of the population, but also an actual need for it. The reason is that strange claims for a so-called new biology are being made by the believers in the Communist creed. For reasons which nobody outside the Soviet Union can understand (and probably very few inside) the science of genetics has been abolished in that country and been replaced by the partly ridiculous, partly mystical assemblage of nonsensical claims made by a scientifically ignorant agronomist (successful, if the uncontrollable reports are true, in practical applications of plant physiology). As this so-called Lysenkoism is being assiduously propagated over the world by scientifically ignorant adherents of said political creed, it is important that thinking people are provided with the information which permits them to judge for themselves. Anybody who has read and understood only the first chapters of this book should be able to see through the sham of the so-called new biology.

The author acknowledges with gratitude the fine editing work of his friend, Professor Richard Paulsen of the University of Chicago.

R. B. GOLDSCHMIDT

Berkeley, California
November, 1951

Contents

viii

Introduction

It is no exaggeration to say that there is no one who has not, at some time, concerned himself with questions of heredity. After all, when you look at a child to see which parent it resembles, when you look for a man's supposed racial characteristics, when you recognize in a friend or relative features you had once noticed in his uncle or grandfather, when you observe that some of the puppies in a litter are piebald and some are solid colored, or when you buy seed of a particular variety of flower or vegetable, in every such instance you assume, consciously or unconsciously, that hereditary characters are involved, passed somehow from ancestor to offspring. You sense, however obscurely, that some rule, some orderly process, must lie behind these inheritances. You may even try to find the rule or process. It will not take you long to discover that the situation seems hopelessly confused. Your own children may faithfully exhibit your own or your spouse's brown eyes, curly hair, Roman nose, slender limbs, very short little finger, emotional responsiveness, etc.; your neighbor's numerous family, on the other hand, may seem to have inherited no feature, physical or mental, from their parents, and the several brothers and sisters may seem to have little or nothing in common. In short, no generally applicable interpretation may seem possible. Yet judgment should be reserved, for more thorough investigation may establish order out of the confusing facts. Closer study may show which traits are transmitted to future generations and which are buried with their possessor, and may reveal how it is that now one, now another type of inheritance appears in what seem to be only bewildering mixtures.

Just such difficulties led to many detours in the quest for laws of biological inheritance before the science of heredity, genetics, could firmly establish the fundamental facts and prin-

1

ciples. But by this time [1] many of the obstacles to clear understanding have been removed, and the main avenues leading into this still rather new field of human exploration have been mapped out, paved with smoothly fitted stones of facts, and made into well-traveled boulevards. It is scarcely needful to add that in genetics, as in any progressive science, new discoveries are continually opening up new vistas, and our understanding grows year by year. But whatever new discoveries may be made, they can be added to a solid foundation which is so simple and clear that no one who wants to go through life with open eyes should fail to acquire an understanding of the fascinating facts. A little concentration may, it is possible, be needed here and there until you learn to think in a somewhat unfamiliar way. However, with a little attention anyone should be able to take the small hurdles and to learn what the science of heredity has to teach. And surely a little effort is in order, so that you may achieve understanding of a body of knowledge which must be yours if you would have true insight into human nature and the living world at large.

[1] 1950 was celebrated as a semicentennial of genetics, the half-century anniversary of the rediscovery of its first important laws.

Hereditary
and Non-Hereditary Traits

Introduction

At the outset, let us have a clear notion of one very important point. When heredity is mentioned, the nurseryman will think of his varieties of flowers, the farmer will think of his seed and crops, the physician will think of his patients with "hereditary" or "constitutional" diseases. The layman, invariably, thinks first of his own human species, with its qualities, characters, deficiencies. If he reads this book he wants to understand, first and foremost, heredity in man. He will find, however, that the following pages will discuss man secondarily to rats and mice, to flowers, peas, and beans, and even to little flies. There is a reason for this. Looking at nature we can find structures, phenomena, activities, and functions which are specific for particular plants or animals. Man alone, for example, has that unique tool, the hand, which, in conjunction with the development of his brain, has made him the master of nature. If we want to study the mechanism of the hand, only man can be our material. Antlers and horns, to take other illustrations, are products of the skin which are found only in certain groups of mammals. We could not study their formation in mice; actually, we could not learn much even from a study of the antlers of the deer about the horns of the sheep.

On the other hand, there are other features of living beings which are common to very different groups. The main characteristics of human blood, upon which all serum treatments are based, are also found in many other animals, and some of them even in plants. The physiologist, therefore, is able to do much of his research with rabbits, guinea pigs, monkeys, and even frogs and yet can apply his results on the human level. Finally, there are phenomena in nature which are of such a generalized kind that they are the same in all animals and even in all plants. Man, fish, insects, and plants seem to breathe in very different ways, if we concentrate our attention upon the way in which air is carried into the organs of breathing. But if we focus on the essential point, the physical and chemical processes of the exchange of oxygen for carbon dioxide, the same set of facts is found all over the animate world. The laws of these processes may be studied in a frog, a fish, a leaf, or a microscopic alga but will apply to man as well as to any other organism. Similarly, all cells multiply by a very typical process of division which is the same in man, bird, insect, infusorian, and plant.

The process of heredity belongs to this most inclusive category. Every type of living being, from the bacteria through the microscopically small inhabitants of a drop of water to more familiar plants and animals, low and high, has the faculty for reproducing its kind, which is really the ability to transmit all its characteristics to its offspring by heredity. When this hereditary transmission is studied in the minutest detail, all the essential processes are seen to be exactly the same, whatever the plant or animal studied. This certainly does not mean that details are not different here and there. We shall later have to study such differences. But the essentials, the basic features, the principles, the laws, are found to be identical in all organisms. We may therefore trust the thousandfold experience that basic facts about heredity discovered in one organism are true for all. Knowing this, we should not be upset when we learn that laws of heredity, which are so important for man, were first discovered in pea plants; that many of the most important and finest details of genetics can be studied best in a small fruit fly; that a detailed knowledge of fertilization, without which heredity cannot be understood, was first and most clearly achieved in a study of the eggs of sea urchins and parasitic worms; that certain bugs and moths have taught the explorer of genetics more than have peacocks, elephants, or, for that matter, man. In short, just as the physiologist uses his guinea pigs and monkeys for experiments that will ultimately be applied to man for his benefit, the

4

geneticist uses his flies, corn, peas, rats, mice, etc., to study the generally valid laws of heredity.

It can easily be seen why he chooses such organisms. A study of heredity requires that we mate hereditarily different organisms at will. Our results are valid, as we shall soon see, only when they are based upon a large number of individuals and when they are followed over a large number of generations. These needs clearly imply that our best "guinea pigs" will be organisms which can easily be bred in large numbers and attain maturity quickly. Examples are the animals and plants mentioned: The fruit fly has 40 generations a year in the laboratory, a single pair of parents having 200–300 offspring. Very thorough comparison and study has always confirmed that the organisms which sentimentally are preferable to the layman, especially his own kind, cannot claim any special position when it comes to heredity. The inheritance of talent for music, or of a white lock on the forehead, follows exactly the laws which govern the inheritance of the coat colors of a rat or of the form of a tiny bristle on the back of a fly.

What is inherited?

In our search for the secrets of heredity, the first task is to find out what is inherited. We note first that each organism belongs to a definite group, called a *species*. Without entering here into a discussion of what a species really is, it may be said from our general experience that man and horse are clearly distinct species. Man always procreates man; horses produce horses. In propagation, then, all the traits and features which characterize a certain species are inherited by all the offspring. Let us be quite clear about what the word "inherited" means in this connection. Man, for example, has a skeleton consisting of hundreds of bones, each of definite size, shape, position, and function. They are so typical and constant that an anatomist could easily pick out any single human bone hidden in a carload of assorted bones. Man has muscles and inner organs which, though rather similar to those of other mammals, are unique and typical for man in definite details and could be distinguished by an expert. Man has blood of such a composition that the smallest trace can be unfailingly identified as human blood. To enumerate all the specific features of man, or of a

5

horse or a fly, would require a whole volume, and all these traits are inherited by the offspring, which otherwise would not be man, horse, or fly.

Now, looking at mankind as a whole, we notice that men, though all characterized by the traits of the human species, form different groups which can readily be distinguished and which transmit their several distinctive traits to their offspring. Think, for example, of African Negroes, Asiatic Mongolian people, and European Whites. Their characters, like skin and eye color, though not species characters of man, are nevertheless hereditary. When we examine these groups closely, we find them subdivided into smaller, recognizable groups, characterized by traits which, again, they transmit to their offspring. Think of the differences between North and South Europeans, between Negroes of East and West Africa, among Chinese, Japanese, and Malays. Within each such group, furthermore, various smaller, distinguishable tribes and local populations can be found. This sort of analysis can be carried, finally, down to the individual family, with its special inherited facial features, character qualities, and even diseases. In daily life it is these more minute and minor traits that we especially notice. We may have no doubt that our children will be men, of Caucasoid type with North European features, but we still wonder and ask whether they will be blond, brunette, blue- or dark-eyed, tall or short, intelligent or slow-witted, healthy or sickly.

Thus we return to the preliminary question, for which we must have an answer before we can attack the problems of heredity: What is inherited? We can also ask: Are there characteristics that belong solely to the individual manifesting them, that disappear with him and are not transmitted to his offspring? If so, what is the relation between hereditary and non-hereditary traits?

Hereditary and non-hereditary traits

At first glance these questions may seem idle. It may be asserted that, if parental traits reappear in progeny, these traits are "hereditary"; if they do not, they are "non-hereditary." Is the distinction really so easily made? For an answer, consider Fig. 1, the pedigree of a family in which the much-discussed "bleeder's disease" (hemophilia) occurs. Bleeders are indi-

viduals whose blood fails to clot properly and who may therefore bleed to death from slight wounds. Before analyzing this
pedigree, however, we may take a moment to examine the
arrangement of this pedigree.

The symbol ♂ (representing the shield and lance of Mars)
identifies a male; ♀ (the mirror of Venus) stands for a female.
White circles indicate normal persons, and black circles represent persons exhibiting the hereditary trait under study. Each
horizontal row of individuals represents one generation; four

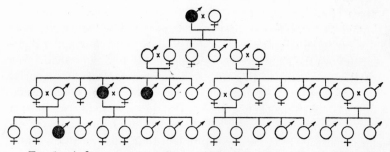

Fig. 1. A diagrammatic pedigree of bleeder's disease (hemophilia).
Black = a bleeder.

rows, then, depict great-grandparents, grandparents, parents,
and children. All the children of one couple are connected by
a horizontal line, to which the individual children are attached
by vertical lines. Children are connected with their parents by
an upward line. Husband and wife are connected by a horizontal bar below their symbols and by the multiplication sign
between them. Men or women marrying into the family are,
of course, not connected with the preceding generation. Now
let us look at this pedigree.

In the first generation a man who is a bleeder marries a normal woman. Two daughters and two sons are born, all normal;
the disease does not seem to be inherited. One of the daughters
(second row, left) is married to a normal man; they produce
two daughters and four sons (third row, left). Both daughters
and two of the sons, grandchildren of the original bleeder, are
normal, but the other two sons are bleeders. Thus, the disease
has been inherited but has jumped one generation. One son
in the second generation marries a normal woman (second row,

right); of this union three sons and three daughters are born (third row, right), all normal. Here, then, the disease was not inherited! Two of these normal grandchildren marry and produce, all told, eight great-grandchildren, all normal (fourth row, right). On the left side of the pedigree, a normal woman of the third generation is married to a normal man. Also, an affected man, brother of the foregoing girl, is married to a normal woman. The normal woman has four children by her normal husband (fourth row, left), one of them a bleeder son. The bleeder of the third generation, however, has five normal children of both sexes (fourth row, second group from left). Now we wish to know: Is the bleeder disease hereditary? On the left side of the pedigree it seems so, though with some jumps and irregularities; on the right side it does not appear to be inherited. We shall later return to this case and easily explain it as a special type of heredity. At this point, the pedigree serves only to demonstrate that one cannot always decide offhandedly whether a trait is hereditary or not. The hereditability or non-hereditability of characters is clearly a problem that must be studied and cannot be prejudged.

Variation

To approach more closely an understanding of the real meaning and significance of hereditary and non-hereditary traits we shall turn to a different example. Farmer Jones raises white beans of particular sizes. He grows three lines or varieties which, as he knows from experience, will yield a small, a medium-sized, and a large bean, respectively. We should then say that he has three hereditarily different strains with respect to bean size. Obviously he must keep his strains pure; in the popular but wholly misleading phrase of truck gardeners and breeders, he must prevent the occurrence of blood mixture. With beans it is not difficult to ensure such purity, for their flowers are both male and female, and self-fertilization is the rule. With proper precautions Farmer J.'s three plots will yield small, medium, and large beans. But now let us harvest 1000 beans from each plot and measure their lengths very carefully. We shall soon see that within any single plot all the beans are not of exactly the same size. Although most of them have the size characteristic of the plot and line, in each lot there are

8

some larger, some smaller than the average. If the average size of small-strain beans is 10 mm., some of the 1000 beans from the small-strain plot are 6, 7, 8, and 9 mm. long, and others are 11, 12, 13, 14 mm. long. Similarly, the average size of medium-strain beans is 15 mm., but some of the 1000 beans from this plot measure 11, 12, 13, 14 and 16, 17, 18, 19 mm. Among the large-strain beans the average length is 20 mm., but there are beans in this lot of 16, 17, 18, 19, 21, 22, 23, and 24 mm. lengths.

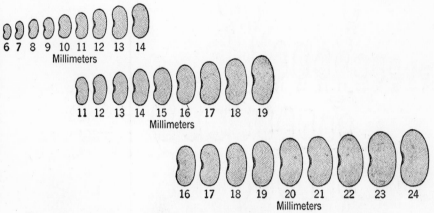

Fig. 2. Variation in size of three strains of beans, a small, a medium, and a large variety. Differences a little exaggerated.

Figure 2 illustrates the results of this study (somewhat exaggerating the size differences for the sake of clarity). We must conclude that even within a hereditarily pure strain every individual does not precisely match the strain "ideal"—the lengths 10, 15, 20 mm. in the present example. Rather, individual differences still exist; there is, as we say, a certain amount of *variation*.

Recognition of this variation can teach us more. If the farmer were to hand us a single bean 13 mm. long without telling us from which plot the bean was taken, we could not by mere inspection determine whether we hold a small individual bean belonging to the medium-sized strain or a large bean of the small strain. In the same way, if he gives us a 17-mm. bean, we do not know whether it is a large specimen of the medium-sized strain or a small representative of the large variety. We are led to the important conclusion that individuals *known* to be geneti-cally, hereditarily, different may, despite this difference, look exactly alike. In other words, the visible, external type does not necessarily give us any information about the hereditary constitution of an individual. Our original question remains: How can we determine what is inherited?

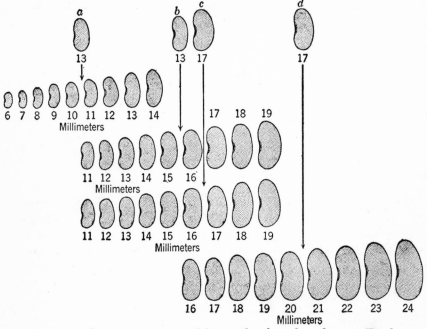

Fig. 3. A selection experiment with beans taken from those drawn in Fig. 2. *a, b, c, d,* the selected beans; and below, their offspring. *a* and *b*, alike in size, belong to different hereditary strains (small and medium); so do *c* and *d*, respectively (medium and large). Illustration of the meaning of pheno-type and genotype.

Let us make a test. We plant some of the 13-mm. beans that the farmer gave us without telling us from which plot or plots they came. The following year one plant from one such seed produces beans with a size variation from 6 to 14 mm. and an average length of 10 mm. Only now is it clear that that particular parental bean came from the hereditarily small strain. To its off-spring it has transmitted the genetic average size, not its variant

10

larger size. A second plant grown from one of the 13-mm. beans given us by the farmer yields seeds with an average length of 15 mm. and a range of variation of 11 to 19 mm. It is again clear—and the farmer can confirm our conclusion—that the parental 13-mm. bean was a small individual of the medium-sized strain. Its offspring received not its individual aberrant size but the length typical of the medium strain. These experiments, together with a similar one involving the large strain, are represented in Fig. 3. This test could be continued and repeated for as many generations as we like; the result will always be the same.

The visible and the hereditary type

In an earlier section we learned that the appearance of an individual does not tell us its hereditary nature. The experiment just cited demonstrates that the genetic constitution, irrespective of external appearance, will show up in progeny. By a "progeny test" we determined whether 13-mm. beans were large representatives of the hereditarily small strain or small variants of the hereditarily medium strain. We have here met one of the basic rules of heredity, one applying to any inheritable features of any organism. The rule is: The apparent type (technically, the. phenotype) need not be the same as the hereditary type (genotype). In the bean case, two different hereditary types gave rise to the same apparent type. We shall later encounter many situations in which different genotypes have the same phenotypes.

The importance of this rule can be made still clearer by reference to the pedigree of the bleeder's disease (Fig. 1). There we noted the curious circumstances that of two normal cousins (it may be noted that the hereditary picture could have been the same for sisters) one had only normal offspring whereas the second had a bleeder son. We suspect, therefore, that in the first woman normal appearance was combined with a heredity for normalcy, but that the other woman, though normal herself, somehow carried invisibly the hereditary constitution for bleeding. In other words, in the first cousin, apparent type and hereditary type were the same; in the second, phenotype and genotype differed. Their offspring—a progeny test—proved that

11

such was the case. In a later chapter we shall analyze the details of this pedigree.

Yet another instructive experiment can be made with the beans. This time we shall use only the medium-sized strain (though we should obtain the same essential results from either of the others). We begin by selecting several small lots of beans, all exactly 15 mm. in length. One such lot is then sown in each of several garden plots prepared in specifically different ways. One plot has fine top soil and is abundantly treated with fertilizer; another has poorer soil and is inadequately fertilized; a third is located in a particularly sunny spot; a fourth is situated in deep shade; and we can try as many other combinations of illumination, soil, water supply, fertilizer, etc., as we wish. The plants are grown, the beans harvested from each plot, and then we again take the trouble to measure every bean carefully (weighing would provide a better index, but a linear dimension is easier to show in a picture). To save time and words, we may confine ourselves to the product of the best and the poorest plots. The results are illustrated by Fig. 4 (with slight exaggeration in size to make the point quite clear). On the left in the figure is the plot with superior conditions, indicated by sunlight and watering. On the right is the plot where plants which are sisters of those in the first plot grew under unfavorable conditions, as indicated by dense shade. The 15-mm. sister beans are shown as planted in each plot; below each bed is its harvest. Quite obviously, the progeny beans are of very different sizes in the two plots: On the good plot the average size is 22 mm., or even larger than for our previous large strain; on the poor plot the average is a mere 8 mm., smaller than in our hereditarily small strain. Yet we know that all the beans planted were of the hereditary medium size.

The reader may not be much surprised by this result, which is very likely just what he expected. But seemingly obvious facts can become significant when properly viewed. We might, for example, begin to doubt the repeated assertion that we are using a strain of beans with a hereditary size of 15 mm. And we do need to qualify that statement. What we must now say is this: The hereditary size of the "medium" strain averages 15 mm. if the beans are grown under a particular set of conditions, say, the average conditions of an ordinary vegetable patch. If con-

12

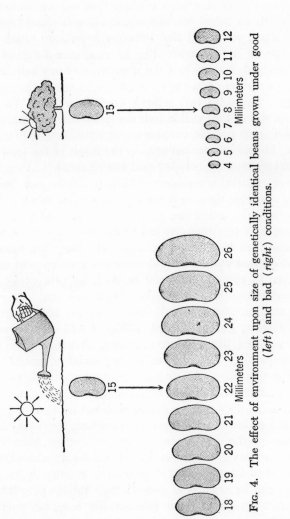

Fig. 4. The effect of environment upon size of genetically identical beans grown under good (*left*) and bad (*right*) conditions.

ditions are better, the size will be greater; in a poorer environment the size will be less.

From our bean experiments we have learned three fundamental facts, facts invariably confirmed whenever similar questions have been asked for any organisms and characters whatsoever. First, we found that different hereditary types (genotypes) can be hidden within the same apparent type (phenotype). Second, we saw that the phenotype of one and the same genotype depends upon the environment in which the organism develops. The third rule follows from these two: We should never call this or that visible trait the hereditary without specifying under what specific environmental conditions that trait will appear. Phenotype, accordingly, is the result of the joint action of hereditary type (genotype) and environment.

The very general importance of these principles may be underlined by applying them to a situation in human society. Among man's inheritable traits are psychological attributes, including, for example, a tendency toward moral weakness or perversion which can lead to criminal activity. On the other hand, it is well known that evil social and economic environment can also cause men to commit antisocial deeds from which they would shrink and refrain in a more favorable environment. Among the genetic social misfits are some whom even the best environment cannot change, just as a born musician will still be musical, though he lives like Robinson Crusoe. There are, of course, many kind and degrees of inherited antisocial or asocial tendencies and propensities. As one instance, it is known that a tendency toward wanderlust, an unsteadiness and proneness to nomadism, is inheritable. One man so constituted but living in a good situation and endowed with some compensating traits may become an explorer of the world's remote corners; another, born to dwell in less favorable circumstances, becomes a tramp, a beachcomber. We are led to the hope that at least some genetically asocial individuals can be trained to control their inborn proclivities or, at any rate, to direct them into socially acceptable channels. But, as the beans have shown us, we can never change the heredity of such individuals, although this is what they will pass on to the following generations. In the contrasting case, the man with desirable heredity but bad habits, we can be certain that his unwanted visible characteristics will not reappear in his

14

offspring if the children are reared in a good environment. Evil is not such a man's nature but is only a cloak hung round his shoulders by a bad environment.

Selection of types

Now we must return to our beans for another experiment. The study illustrated by Fig. 4 showed us that the genetically medium-sized (15 mm. average length) line reacted to excellent growth conditions by producing seed of sizes up to 26 mm. This result may have raised the hope that we can raise still larger beans simply by selecting the largest ones so far obtained and growing another crop from them. Can we actually continue in this way until we have giant beans? Unfortunately, this is the kind of reckoning the milkmaid in the parable used. We proceed to sow the 26-mm. beans from the previous experiment, growing one lot under standard conditions, those we started with in breeding 15-mm. beans; another sample is given the especially favorable treatment we accorded the parents. What sort of beans do we harvest from these plots? The offspring of the first lot will be identical to the members of the strain, averaging 15 mm. in length. Contrary to hopeful expectation, the effect of good conditions has not been inherited at all. In the second plot, with its superior conditions, the beans are once more as large as the lot including the 26-mm. parents, with the average length 22 mm. and the variation ranging from 18 to 26 mm. The reader may object on the grounds that a single attempt to increase size by breeding the largest individuals is insufficient. Then we repeat the experiment. The result is precisely the same. And even if we were to repeat the attempt each year for decades, the result would not change, the offspring of the repeatedly selected largest beans remaining at the average size of 22 mm. when grown under the highly favorable conditions of our experiment. No matter how we vary the experiment, the result will be the same. In other words, environment acts only on the appearance of the individual, whereas the hereditary constitution remains constant, quite unaffected by those external conditions which modified the phenotype.

A skeptic may require one more check on our results. Let us, he says, for 10 or 20 years always breed from the largest beans obtained under the best of growth conditions, and then raise

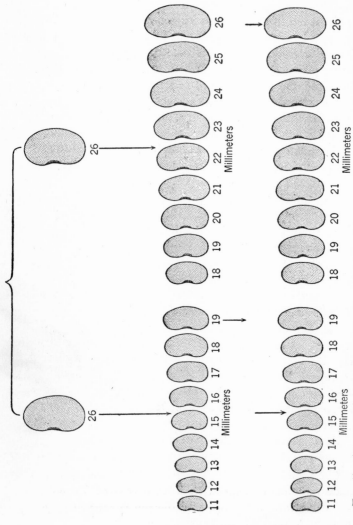

Fig. 5. (*Left*) Large beans produced under favorable environmental conditions from medium-sized strain over many generations are bred under normal conditions. The offspring fluctuates around the medium size of the strain; the large parental size is not inherited. (*Right*) Large sister beans bred under very favorable conditions produce a large size of offspring, which, however, is not hereditary.

16

one crop under standard conditions. Should not the beans grown in an average situation be somewhat larger than the original variety? The experimental answer, as illustrated by Fig. 5, is entirely in the negative. The beans subjected to standard conditions immediately return to the original 15 mm. average size.

At first sight these facts may seem astonishing, though the experimental results have been confirmed a thousand times in all sorts of organisms and for all manner of hereditary traits. They contradict the ideas of the uninstructed layman; they are completely at variance with all we have heard of the achievements of the successful plant and animal breeders. For every breeder and husbandryman will tell you that he improves his seed or stock by repeatedly choosing for propagation, selecting, as he calls it, the best individuals he has. He would scoff at the notion that no improvement can be wrought by this method. Who is right? Hundreds and thousands of careful experiments enable us to assert that we are unquestionably right. But the breeder is not wrong; rather, we make entirely different points. And this is a statement we must understand clearly, for its proper evaluation is as important to practical breeding as to our grasp of the basic principles of heredity.

More about variation and chance

To be quite clear about this problem we go back to the beginning of our bean experiments, first reemphasizing that we could just as well have studied in the same way and with the same general results any hereditary character of any organism whatso ever. We found that beans of a particular pure strain had the same average size, say 15 mm., when grown under standard conditions; this is, therefore, their hereditary size. But 15 mm. was only the average length of a large number of beans (see Fig. 2); some individual seeds were a little shorter or a little longer, within a limited range. Up to now we have neglected to determine how many beans of these various sizes—15 mm., a little more, and a little less—appear in the full harvest of a plot. Our next task is, then, to measure the beans and sort them according to size into nine sacks, one for each of the lengths 11, 12, 13, 14, 15, 16, 17, 18, and 19 mm. The sacks are next set in line in the order of size of the contained beans, the sack with the smallest beans being on the extreme left, that with the largest on the extreme right (Fig. 6). The bag with the greatest number of beans, it is immediately seen, contains beans of the mean size, 15 mm. To the right and left of it the sacks become progressively smaller, as the size of the beans departs further and further from the average. This shows that among the

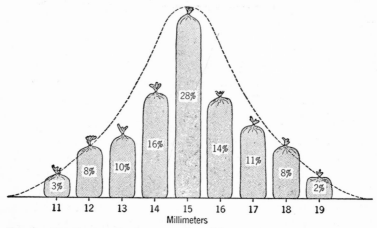

Fig. 6. Distribution of a huge number of beans of an average size of 15 mm. Each bag holds beans of identical size. The bags are arranged in the order of the sizes of the beans contained therein. (The error introduced by the fact that 10 large beans do not occupy twice as much space as 5 small ones, i.e., the neglect of the 3 dimensions of a bean, should be overlooked for the sake of the simplicity of the visual demonstration.)

thousands of beans of our pure strain those of medium size are most frequent, the smallest and the largest beans are rarest, and the other sizes fit into an orderly sequence of increasing and decreasing frequency. In Fig. 6 are inscribed the percentages of the entire harvest contained in each bag; these numbers form a series that begins with a low percentage, increases to a maximum, and then declines: 3, 8, 10, 16, 28, 14, 11, 8, 2. To the right and left of the highest value, 28%, this series of numbers is almost symmetrical. This fact is easily seen when we connect the tops of the bags by a broken line, making a curve or graph, which is nearly symmetrical, ascending on the left of the middle class from almost nothing and descending similarly to the right. Expressing this fact in more scientific language, we can say that all our beans show a curve of variation with respect to size, with a mean size of approximately 15 mm. and a range of variation from 11 to 19 mm.

It is remarkable that this curve will be more nearly symmetrical the larger the number of beans we measure. Still more remarkable is the fact that practically all measurable characters of animals and plants when studied in this way will always give such a curve, whether it is the size of the leaves of a tree, the size of microscopic organisms of a pure strain, the number of hairs or bristles or similar organs on a certain area of an insect, or the size of piebald spots in a spotted breed of guinea pigs or cattle. But it must be kept in mind that organisms exhibiting such variation are hereditarily pure strains in regard to the character measured.

What is the meaning of this symmetrical curve of variation? Rather surprisingly, it can be made clear by a look at certain gambling devices, like dice throwing and roulette. The simplest device for a visual demonstration is the elementary pinball machine pictured in Fig. 7. At one end of a flat box is a funnel-like inlet. At the opposite end a series of compartments are separated by vertical strips of wood. In between are a large number of nails stuck into the board at equal intervals. A handful of fine birdshot is poured into the funnel and, when the top of the gadget is lifted, runs down between the nails into the compartments. There the shot will always assume the arrangement shown in Fig. 7. We see at once that this is the same arrangement as that of the bean bags: a symmetrical ascending and descending curve, with most shot in the center compartments, least at the extreme right and left, and increasing and decreasing amounts in between. With this model it is easy to understand how the arrangement of the shot is brought about. It is due to the simple action of chance. An individual pellet of shot running down may hit a nail and be deflected to the right; soon it may strike another nail and by chance be deflected to the left. If there are many nails and a perfectly smooth-running board, the hits to the right and to the left will cancel each other and the pellet will arrive at the center compartment. But the pellets are not ideally perfect spheres, the nails not ideally perfect cylinders, and the board not ideally smooth. Thus, it may happen that a pellet is more often deflected to one side than to the other. In

19

a very large number of cases (many pellets of shot) chance alone will decide these events. There is only a very small chance that the same pellet will always be deflected to the same side. In other words, the chance for a pellet to land in the compartments at the extreme left or right is very small. The chance will in-

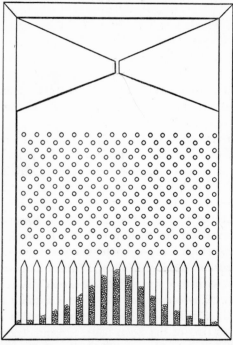

FIG. 7. Galton's pinball game for the demonstration of the law of chance.

crease with more and more equalization of the number of deflections to right and left, and the best chance is for an equal number, which sends the shot into the center compartment. The pinball machine thus visualizes for us the effects of chance on a large number of similar events.

Now let us apply this demonstration of the effects of chance to our experiment with beans. The developing beans, marked by their heredity to grow to a size of 15 mm., in the course of rolling down the stages of growth strike the nails of environmental conditions. Here one corner of the field receives less water, there the fertilizer has not spread evenly, etc. Just as in the

20

gadget, it is least probable that these chance changes will always affect a single bean in a favorable or in an unfavorable way, whereas an equalization between both extremes is most probable. Thus, small variations in size arise and appear in the numbers typical for the symmetrical curve of variation. Variation and its curve within a hereditarily pure strain are the result of the action of the environment and the distribution of these effects according to chance.

Mixed and pure strains

Now we are ready to return to the problem that puzzled us earlier: Is the breeder right or wrong when he tells us that he can improve his strains by always selecting the best individuals for breeding? To find an answer, let us proceed as follows: Just as we measured the medium-sized strain of beans (15 mm. average), we proceed to measure the small (10-mm.) and the large (20-mm.) strain. As expected, the measurements of the small ones give a curve of variation with its highest point at 10 mm. and the large ones similarly with the maximum at 20 mm. Next we take all the bags from all three strains and mix their contents thoroughly. Each bean from this mixed product of all strains is measured, nine bags are assigned to the different sizes, now ranging from 6 to 24 mm., and all beans are sorted out into these bags as before. The result will be the same curve of variation, though we know now that we have measured a mixture of three different hereditary strains. Thus it is seen that we cannot by mere inspection distinguish in such a case a mixture of different strains from a single pure strain. A progeny test, however, will enable a distinction immediately. If we select the largest beans, for example, for next year's breeding, they will produce large ones, because we have picked out of a mixture those belonging to the hereditarily large strain. If we repeat the experiment with the largest progeny beans obtained, no further size increase will be observed. We shall find only the variation typical of the large strain. We selected this variety from a mixture of strains and thereby ended any chance for further success in selection. The first success was merely apparent, owing to our having worked with a mixture of different heredities.

These facts enable us to understand why the breeder is right and at the same time wrong when he believes that he can improve his material by continued selection. If he had started with a hereditarily pure strain, he would have had no success whatever. But he usually begins with an unanalyzed field that is, in fact, a complicated mixture of many different strains. He will be successful with his selections until he has finally succeeded in isolating that one of the hereditary strains contained in his field which is to his liking, and this will be the end of his success.

In explaining these elementary facts of heredity, I have had to speak of hereditarily pure strains without explaining properly what this term means. As a matter of fact, the real scientific explanation cannot be given until later, when you shall have mastered the laws of heredity. But even here we can closely approximate a proper notion of the meaning of "pure strains" or "pure races," at least in a general way. We may, for example, be inclined to call poodles or great Danes members of a pure strain or race of dogs. But when we study them closely, we find that there are hereditarily different and constant substrains of poodles and great Danes in regard to size, color, temperament, etc. The professional breeder will be able to subdivide even these groups according to some characters. Any of these strains, substrains, and sub-substrains will correspond to our strains of beans if it is pure in all its characters, i.e., if these characters reappear in all the offspring without change except the minor variations caused by environment. Normally, however, a breeder will be concerned not with all hereditary differences contained in one strain but only with its overall appearance. If he breeds German shepherd dogs, he is content with the general wolflike appearance of this beautiful animal. He will therefore not object to mating a pair differing in small but hereditary characters, and the offspring, though all shepherd dogs, will exhibit to the experienced eye various combinations of all these minor differences. His strain, then, is pure for the general characteristics of the shepherd dog but not for many smaller traits of size, color, length of hair, form of ears, etc. Now the changing fashions among the fanciers may require that a prize shepherd dog must have particular color, ear form, tail, etc. The breeder sets out to breed this type. His procedure is not mysterious. What he does is to search among his animals for those which show one or another of the previously neglected traits, mate them, pick out in the next generation good combinations, breed them again, and repeat this

22

procedure until he has the requisite combination of traits and sees it transmitted to all offspring. He has not produced anything new (though he will probably claim so); he merely selected and combined what was already present. But it may also happen that the mysterious beauty code of dog-fanciers' clubs decides that a prize animal must have some character which is not hereditary at all. In this event the breeders will deceive themselves and will receive medals for the chance play of nature if they happen by luck to find among their puppies the non-hereditary and non-transmissible character required by the rules.

It is a short step from a dog to his master, and so we may return for a moment to man and perform, though only in our minds, an experiment. There are found in Africa many Negro tribes which, to the uninitiated, differ most conspicuously in the size of individuals. There are tribes with what we think of as average stature, and there are also giant Dinka and tiny Pygmies. Let us for the moment forget about all their characteristic features, save size, and assume that these three tribes intermarry freely. After a number of generations the area will be inhabited by a population that varies from a tiny size, through all gradations, to giants. A statistician who measured such a population would find a typical symmetrical curve of height just as found previously for bean length. If we studied individual families, we should find tall parents with tall children, tall parents with children of varying size, and many other different combinations. This is not surprising, because the population would be a hybrid one produced by commingling several types that can recombine freely in various ways, as we shall soon study in detail. If we now chose to select from this population a purely tall tribe, we could easily do so by selecting over a few generations the tallest couples until we had again isolated from the mixture the pure-breeding Dinka type. And here our selection would be at an end, for we could not obtain still taller families; we cannot produce from the population anything that was not in it originally.

Summary

Let us summarize in a few words what we have learned thus far about hereditary traits. We know as a fact that the visible characters of an individual do not necessarily conform to its

23

heredity. A given visible character may be the product of completely different hereditary constitutions; for example, a medium-sized form may be hereditarily medium-sized, it may be hereditarily large but stunted by poor environment, or it may be small by heredity but overgrown by good environment. Only a test of the progeny of the individual will reveal its hereditary constitution. The apparent type or phenotype is the product of the hereditary type or genotype combined with the action of the environment. The effect of the environment in shifting the apparent type in one direction or another does not affect the hereditary type. For this reason we cannot select new hereditary types from a pure breed by breeding from extreme apparent types. When selection of extreme types does succeed in establishing a new hereditary type, the reason is that the group from which a selection was made was not hereditarily pure but a mixture of different hereditary types, though this fact could not have been discerned by simple inspection. From such a mixture the genetic ingredients can be isolated by selection, but once the pure component hereditary strains have been isolated, no further selection is possible. These, then, are basic facts of heredity which should be understood before the details of hereditary transmission can be sought.

Non-heredity of so-called "acquired" characters

We have analyzed these basic facts in a straight line, without looking right or left. We may pause now for a few points that are of general interest and importance. I have already mentioned the fact that the non-inheritance of the effects of favorable conditions runs counter to widely held popular beliefs. This particular situation has become increasingly interesting in recent years, since the opposite view has been made the official, government-sponsored doctrine of one nation (the U.S.S.R.) and has been imposed by force upon its scientists and laity. Again we inquire: Is it really established beyond doubt that characters acquired under the action of the environment are not inherited? Does it really not make any difference to the hereditary constitution of man whether his ancestral generations lived in the best of environments or in utter squalor?

To find an answer, we may forget man for a moment, because we are dealing here with an area in which man, though strictly

24

bound to the same natural laws as all other organisms, has been
enabled to circumvent the rule, at least in part, by his brain
power. Let us start with a rather crude example. Most
people have heard once upon a time that a neighbor's cat lost
her tail by an accident and in her next litter had tailless kittens.
When such stories have a background of truth, the explanation
is not at all mysterious. There exists a race of cats, the manx
cat from the Isle of Man, which has a genetic, hereditary reduced
tail, a mere knob or even less. This character has spread to many
cat populations and may crop up here or there. If, by chance,
the mutilated cat mated with a tom carrying this hereditary trait,
reduced tail will appear in some of the offspring according to
definite rules of heredity. This is certainly a crude example, for
few people will expect mutilations to become inherited. But, in
principle, it is just as good as any other illustration of environmental action upon the organism, for, in every case where the
"inheritance of acquired characters" has been claimed, the claim
has been shown to stem from failure to consider hereditary traits
already present or from some bad understanding. There is, for
example, a popular belief that children of a soldier may show a
kind of scar in the same place as where the father was wounded.
Provided that the story is not a complete invention, a chance
mole or its like may have been accepted by the credulous as the
inherited scar.

Believers in the inheritance of acquired characters (and the
emphasis is properly on "believer," for what is involved is actually
a creed, not a scientifically tenable opinion) do, of course, have
better examples in their arsenal than mutilations and scars. For
instance, plants reared in an unusual climate will change in size,
time of flowering and fruiting, and other characters. When these
changes have persisted for many generations in the new situation, can we really expect that the newly acquired type will be
shed like an overcoat, that no effect will remain? The answer is
clearly and unequivocally supplied by experiments, carried out
countless times in rapidly reproducing organisms, which could be
followed for many generations. *In no such test has an inheritable
effect of the environment ever been observed*.

The reader may still protest that he has heard how persons
transplanted to a life among very different people, like immigrants
to the United States, change even in bodily form to resemble the

25

people among whom they have come to dwell. But even apart from new nutritional conditions and the posture and behavior of the free man, which certainly are not inherited, such claims, if they be factual, are explainable simply by progressive legitimate and illegitimate mixture in the melting pot.

The extreme caution one must exercise before an alleged "proof" of the inheritance of acquired characters can be accepted may be illustrated by one more example. It is a counterpart of the case of the tailless cats and just as easily explained. Scientists, as a rule, would not, of course, be taken in by these crude examples, but in special cases it may be more difficult to determine just where experimental error has crept in. A thorough investigation, however, has never failed to reduce the best examples to the level of the following rather crude one. Recalling the pedigree of bleeder's disease (Fig. 1), we know that a hereditary trait may be present without becoming visible. When, after a number of generations apparently free of it, such a trait again becomes manifest, chance coincidence may have given rise to this sort of situation: A bleeder marries and soon afterward dies of hemorrhage. After his death a daughter is born, who, though normal herself, can transmit the disease to half her sons. When this daughter reaches adulthood, she may never have heard of her father's unhappy condition, nor of any relatives who were bleeders; she will confidently assert, in full honesty so far as her own knowledge goes, that her family has always been normal. This daughter marries and later is involved in an accident in which she nearly bleeds to death. Presently she gives birth to a son, who turns out to be a bleeder. The aunts and neighbors shake their heads and mutter, "Just what we expected after that accident."

This example may seem a little farfetched, but it is in fact a good model of the way in which "reliable" stories of the inheritance of acquired characters originate. But we need not continue the argument. The facts are plain. Whenever experiments have been conducted to induce hereditary changes by the direct action of the environment upon the *body* of an organism, the experiments being carefully carried out to exclude the previous presence of invisible hereditary traits that might mimic changes induced by the environment, and to check apparent positive results by progeny tests, *the result has in every case been negative.* And

26

indeed, when we presently become acquainted with the operation of the mechanism of heredity, we shall see that the facts make an inheritance of acquired characters virtually impossible.

Tradition

I have already hinted at the peculiar position man occupies because of his remarkable brain development. Like all other organisms, man cannot transmit the effects of his environment, good or bad, through his body to his children. The laws of heredity grant no exceptions to the human body. But in a certain measure the human mind can circumvent this lack. The extraordinary capacity of the human brain permits man to compensate in some respects for what nature denies his body. Language, writing, printing are the mechanisms for cultural inheritance, which can, to a degree, transmit environmental modifications. If a horse should actually be born like the once-notorious "bright Hans," who could acquire some mastery of mathematics and accomplish other mental feats, his descendants would still have to begin learning all over again and would never know what the father had known. Man, however, can write down his personal experiences and intellectual acquisitions and leave them in the crib of the next generation, which in turn adds to and passes on the hoard. In time an immense treasure of knowledge is thus accumulated, though no one receives any of it via hereditary transmission in the biological sense. It is handed down culturally, by tradition. Thus, when the biologist must tell you that nothing your mind acquires by work, thought, feeling, or self-improvement will reappear in your children as a result of hereditary transmission, he can nevertheless add that, by oral and written communication, everything of value for the progress of mankind can be preserved by that specifically human substitute for the non-existent inheritance of acquired characters: tradition, the sum total of the cultural endowment.

The Sex Cells
and Fertilization

The cell theory

It may be safely assumed that every reader is acquainted with the fact that the body of every living being, with the exception of the very lowest ones, is composed of cells, which may be individually distinguishable according to their functions but are nevertheless alike in a general way, simply by virtue of being cells. The skin is composed of skin cells, built and arranged in such a way as to form collectively a protective layer around the body; glands consist of gland cells, capable of secreting definite juices; muscles are bundles of long, slender cells that can contract and expand; nerves are composed of nerve cells; sense organs, of sensory cells; etc. Despite the fact that all these types of cells may have distinctive form, size, function, and detailed structure, they are identical in one respect: All consist of the two major parts which characterize a cell—the semiliquid, gelatinous cell body or cytoplasm, formed of the basic living substance called protoplasm; and the nucleus, a small, clearly delineated, bubble-like structure lying within the cytoplasm.

Another common property of the diverse cells of an organism can be elucidated by tracking them backward through all stages of development of the individual to the very beginning, the initial egg from which the organism developed. The more closely we approach this earliest stage, the more similar are the cells. At a certain very early stage they look quite alike: All are simple spherical or cuboidal blobs of protoplasm, each with a nucleus. At this same stage their number is only a very small fraction of the number present at any later developmental level or in the completed organism.

Now, by reversing our path and following development in its proper sequence from egg toward adult, we can observe that two things happen to cells: They multiply only by division of one cell into two, each of these into two more, etc.; and they become specialized by transformation from the simple spherical or cuboidal form into the size, shape, and finely elaborated structural detail of the many kinds of cells characteristic of the fully developed organism.

If, instead, we continue tracing backward in development from the stage with apparently like cells, we find that the number of these similar cells progressively decreases, from perhaps 64 to 32, then to 16, 8, 4, 2 to, finally 1 lone cell. This is the egg cell, out of which a body of, perhaps, billions of cells will be formed by repeated cell divisions. It is obvious, therefore, that all properties, structures, and functions of the future fully developed organism are somehow present as potentialities in the egg, for this is development's starting point. The non-biologist might suppose that some characteristics of an animal which develops within its mother's body, as do the mammals, will be furnished by the maternal body. This is not at all the case. In fact, in the majority of animals, whose eggs develop wholly outside the maternal organism, there is no possibility for such influences to operate. So it is that at the moment the egg is laid or spawned, its minute speck of substance must contain everything necessary to guarantee normal development, to ensure that a Siamese fighting fish will develop from a Siamese fighting fish egg, a lobster from a lobster egg, worm from a worm egg—each new organism being an exact replica (apart from very minor variation) of its parents. This specificity of development of egg cell into parental type is clearly the manifest expression of heredity. Thus it is clear that the egg, as the starting point for the action of heredity in controlling development, must contain within its often microscopically small substance all that is essential for the mysterious operations of heredity.

Cell division and chromosomes

To lift the veil from this mystery we must begin at the beginning, which is the cell's ability to multiply by dividing into two.

When a cell is ready to divide—and what follows applies equally to virtually all cells of plants and animals, including, of course, man—striking changes draw our attention to that minuscule sac within the protoplasm, the cell nucleus. A complicated series of events occurs in the nucleus, the very nature of which suggests their importance. In its resting stage the nucleus is essentially a bladder filled with a fluid in which are suspended somewhat more solid bodies, these consisting of a unique and extremely important material. To study this substance more closely we make use of a technique which enables us to see far more of the details of such microscopically small structures than we could make out in the living nucleus. The cell is killed by certain chemicals that precisely preserve its structural detail, and then stained with particular dyes. Among the available dyes some stain only definite parts of the cell; one group of dyes colors only the small, more solid bodies within the nucleus and permits us to follow them in all their changes. These small masses and granules of dye-accepting substance in the nucleus are said to consist of *chromatin* (from the Greek word *chromos* or dye). Chromatin is the stuff that plays the most important role in cell division.

At the very beginning of cell division the rather irregularly distributed chromatin masses within the nucleus are assembled upon threadlike structures, which were actually present but invisible. These structures then condense in various ways and become visible as a number of units, some rodlike, some spherical, some resembling tiny horseshoes. The forms they take are characteristic and typical of the cells of each kind of organism. They mark a man, a lily, or a snail as clearly as do more obvious and outward features. It is in these minute bodies that many of the secrets of heredity are hidden. These structures, called *chromosomes* because they are "stain- [*chromos*] accepting bodies [*soma*]," are the most important entities in the world of the living.

Study of the chromosomes, as suggested already, gives us at once a fact of prime importance: The number, size, shape, and even the relative positions of the chromosomes are exactly the same in all the cells of any given species of animal or plant.[1] In

---

[1] Certain qualifications of this statement will be developed in due course. All such qualifications underline the fundamental constancy of the chromosomes.

30

all dividing cells of man 48 chromosomes of definite size and form appear. All cells of a certain lily have 24; those of a particular species of moth, 62. The number and nature of the chromosomes in a nucleus is thus a constant character of each living type. But it should not be thought that higher organisms have more chromosomes and lower organisms fewer. No such rule exists. Moreover, the same number may be found in widely different organisms: 24 chromosomes are typical of a lily, a newt, and a fish. The smallest number, 2, appears in a parasitic worm; the largest numbers, 200 and more, in deep sea crabs, ferns, and sugar cane. In every case, however, the number is the same for all cells of a given organism; and usually it is an even number. To this basic fact we shall often return.

Now we are ready to continue our study of cell division, concentrating on the important phases, as represented in Fig. 8, and leaving aside those details which are of special interest to the professional student of cell biology. As soon as the chromosomes are fully formed, the rest of the nucleus seemingly dissolves. Meanwhile, as the chromosomes form within the nucleus, the cytoplasm or cell body begins its preparations for division. Near the nucleus a tiny body (called the centrosome or central body) appears; around it the cytoplasm forms radiating lines, like rays around the sun. The central body then divides into two parts, which, surrounded by their rays, move apart as though they repulsed one another. Their travels cease only when they reach opposite poles of the cell. When the nucleus then dissolves, the rays expand and fill the entire cell. A special portion of this complicated apparatus (called the mitotic figure, from the Greek word *mitos*, meaning a thread) extends from the polar central bodies to the central cell area where the chromosomes lie. One fiber of the mitotic apparatus is attached to each of the chromosomes. The chromosomes have by this time moved into very regular positions along a single plane at the equator of the cell. When one looks from one of the poles toward the cell equator, one sees the chromosomes arranged in an orderly way at a single level; their arrangement is typical and rather constant for any given species of plant or animal. This figure is called the chromosomal or equatorial plate, and it is this which we generally use when picturing the chromosomes of any particular organism.

31

The next visible event (it has actually occurred somewhat earlier but is readily seen only at this stage) is the lengthwise

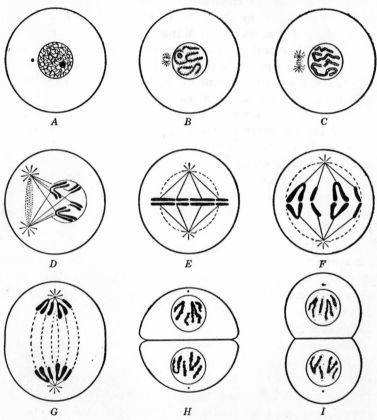

FIG. 8. Nine stages of the division of a cell with the normal number of 4 chromosomes. (*Upper row*) The formation of the chromosomes in the nucleus and their splitting into two identical halves. (*Second row*) Entering of the chromosomes into the equatorial plate and beginning of the moving apart of the split halves. (*Third row*) Completion of the movement of the daughter chromosomes to the poles, reconstruction of the daughter nuclei, and division of the cell body.

division of each chromosome into 2 completely identical daughter chromosomes. We may describe it as the splitting of 1 chromosome into 2, or we may say with greater accuracy that the original chromosome has duplicated itself, has produced a perfect replica of itself. Each daughter chromosome, furthermore, is attached to a fiber extending to one of the central bodies, the fibers of a pair of daughters being connected with opposite cell poles. The daughter chromosomes now move, perhaps being pulled in some way by the fibers, to opposite poles./ If at this stage we look down upon the cell from one or the other pole, we should see near each pole a chromosomal plate precisely like that at the cell equator in the preceding stage. Thus a set of chromosomes exactly the same in number, shape, and size as in the original nucleus arrives at each pole.

The processes observable in the nucleus at the beginning of division are now reversed. The chromosomes seem to disintegrate to a greater or lesser degree, while droplets of liquid appear about them and coalesce to form definitive bladder-like daughter nuclei. Chromosomal structures slowly disappear in the new resting nuclei. This means that the chromosomes are now invisible under the microscope. They are nevertheless present, as may be shown by special means.

Concurrently with these changes, a furrow cuts in from the equatorial surface of the cell and finally divides the cytoplasm into 2 equal masses, while the central bodies and their associated rays gradually disappear. In this way, from a single cell 2 cells have arisen, each identical in structure and content with the mother cell.

Reviewing this complex process, one is forcefully impressed with the importance of the material we have labeled chromatin. For the whole mechanism of cell division is clearly seen to be a device for distributing the substance of the chromosomes with absolute, and almost incredible, precision. This real significance of cell division was appreciated even by the earliest students of the process; furthermore, they understood that the chromosomes must consequently be the important entities for heredity. Only one material can be biologically so indispensable that it must be present in its unique form in every cell of an organism: that is the material responsible for the development of those inheritable traits which are the specific and transmissible properties of each kind of plant and animal. However, to convert this early general insight into the meaning of cell division to incontrovertible fact required nearly 50 years of very hard work on the part of thousands of biologists.

33

Egg and sperm cells

This discussion started with the egg, the original cell from which each living being develops. We must now return to the subject of the egg to complete the foundation for further analysis. First of all, it should be recalled that, save for some exceptions which can be overlooked at this point, every organism is procreated by a mother and a father. The mother supplies the *egg*

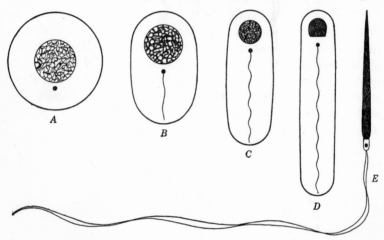

FIG. 9. Diagram of the main features of transformation of a sperm cell into a spermatozoon with head and tail.

cell, the father a *sperm cell,* which fertilizes the egg. What is the significance of these elementary facts?

When we speak of eggs, we are likely to think of a hen's egg, or an ostrich's. In actuality, the eggs of most animals and plants are, like cells generally, microscopically small. In certain groups of animals, however, as in lizards, birds, turtles, and sharks, the egg cell, initially very small, is crammed with nutrient materials, needed because development takes place entirely within the shell deposited by the mother around the egg cell. The yolk of a hen's egg is simply an enormously inflated cell body; its nucleus, nevertheless, is not larger than that of other cells. This huge cell is enclosed within still more food, the egg white, and a protective shell. Essentially, however, the hen's egg, or

34

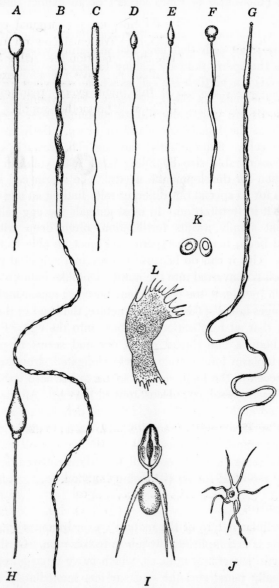

Fig. 10. Types of spermatozoa in different animals: (A) man, (B) ray, (C) gull, (D) snail, (E) jellyfish, (F) pike, (G) beetle, (H) lungfish, (I) crab, (J–L) water fleas and their kin.

the egg (thousands of times larger) of an extinct dinosaur, is nothing more than a single cell.

The rooster's sperm cells are sharply different. They are microscopically small cells that look like miniature whips swimming about in the sperm fluid by lashing to and fro. Each of these tiny threads is nevertheless a cell, as we can see when we trace its origin in the male sex gland, the *testis*. Very young sperm cells in the testis are practically indistinguishable from very young egg cells in the female sex gland or *ovary*. Both are simple, spherical cells. Subsequently, the egg cell grows to its often rather considerable size by filling itself with yolk, an evident preparation for developmental needs. The sperm cell similarly prepares for its special but different role: finding an egg cell and entering it in fertilization. In most animals the egg cell cannot move but simply awaits fertilization, often deep within the maternal body; hence, the sperm cell must be able to travel to the egg. This it can do because the original spherical potential sperm cell is converted into the motile, whiplike definitive sperm. As shown by Fig. 9, the cell nucleus becomes increasingly dense and changes into a spike-shaped structure, the head of the sperm, the part that, at fertilization, will bore into the egg. From the central body a fine thread grows out and seems to push the outer cytoplasm into a progressively elongated structure, which finally becomes the long, slender sperm tail, whose lashing propels the sperm head, or nucleus, toward the egg. All sperm cells are formed in this general way, although details vary somewhat. Figure 10 presents a few examples; all are seen to agree in having a nucleus transformed into a head, and a cytoplasmic body, which in some forms is only slightly differentiated, in others is highly modified for its swimming function.

Fertilization

The cellular nature of the mature sperm becomes clear while the sperm is accomplishing its job in fertilization. Of the many sperm cells, sometimes millions, which move upon an egg, only one actually penetrates the egg surface; immediately after its entrance the egg elaborates a secretion that bars entry of others. Only the sperm head actually enters the egg; the tail, the cytoplasmic part of the cell, remains outside the egg until it disintegrates or otherwise disappears (see Fig. 11). Once it is inside the egg the sperm head resumes the usual spherical shape of a nucleus and slowly moves toward the egg nucleus until the two nuclei come to lie side by side in intimate union. This, the union of a nucleus of maternal origin with one of paternal origin, is fertilization; development of the new individual can now get under way.

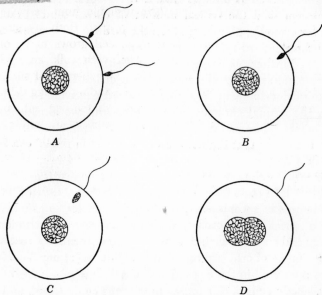

Fig. 11. (A, B) Entrance of one sperm into the egg; (C) transformation of the sperm head into the male nucleus; (D) fertilization = union of egg and sperm nuclei.

At this point we must return to those uniquely important nuclear structures, the chromosomes, which we have already seen reproduced exactly during cell division. Let it be recalled that any nucleus of a given species has a typical and constant number of chromosomes, for example, 48 in man. We might therefore expect the egg and sperm nuclei to have the typical number of chromosomes. And indeed, if we examine very young egg and sperm cells, long before their transformation into the definitive egg and sperm, we do find the standard chromosome number. But does this number hold for the mature egg and sperm which unite in fertilization?

37

The chromosomes in fertilization

The fertilized egg, we have just seen, contains an egg nucleus and a sperm nucleus. We shall follow its history a little further. Chromosomes appear in both nuclei, and all the chromosomes from both nuclei enter a single division figure for the first division of the fertilized egg, which is the real initial step in individual development. It is obvious that if the mature egg and sperm nuclei contained the typical number of chromosomes of other cells, for example, 48 in man, then the fertilized egg would have twice the standard number, or 96 in man, 48 coming from each parent. Further, since cell division faithfully reproduces the chromosome set originally present in a cell, all cells formed in course of development from this fertilized egg would also have twice the normal chromosome number. But we already know that, in fact, all human cells contain only 48 chromosomes. It follows, therefore, that the mature egg and sperm nuclei can have only half the normal chromosome number, or 24 in man. That this is actually the case can be seen when we follow the events of fertilization beyond the stage illustrated in Fig. 11. In Fig. 12, the example is an organism which, for simplicity, is assumed to have a normal chromosome number of only 4. After union of the egg and sperm nuclei, chromosomes appear in both, just as at the beginning of ordinary cell division. But look: Only 2 chromosomes are found in the egg nucleus, and only 2 in the sperm nucleus. Body cells of this organism have 4 chromosomes, and the young egg and sperm cells have 4, but, as we see, the mature egg and sperm contain only 2 (Fig. 12A). How has this difference arisen? This, as we shall see, is one of the most important events for understanding the laws of heredity, but, before we proceed with it, we should complete our study of fertilization.

After the chromosomes become visible in the egg and sperm nuclei, the nuclear wall dissolves, just as in ordinary cell division, the usual division figure with its rays and fibers is formed, and the 4 chromosomes arrange themselves at the equator of the cell. In Fig. 12 the 2 from the mother are shown in white, the 2 from the father in black. Each chromosome now divides, as in any cell division. In consequence, when cell division has been completed, each daughter cell contains the normal chromosome number for the species, 4 in our example. All succeeding cell

38

divisions will be accomplished by the method we have previously followed; every cell formed by cell divisions stemming from the fertilized egg will, therefore, have 2 maternal (white) and 2 paternal (black) chromosomes. In other words, all body cells of any organism contain 2 equal sets of chromosomes, one derived from the mother, one from the father. If, now, we remember that

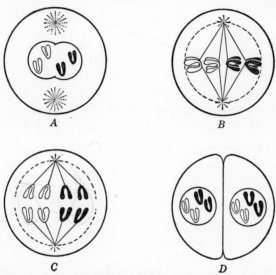

FIG. 12. The behavior of the chromosomes in fertilization. The white chromosomes are those derived from the egg nucleus; the black, those from the sperm nucleus. (A) Appearance of the chromosomes in the male and female nuclei; (B) formation of the division figure; (C, D) the first division of the fertilized egg.

only the sperm head, which is the sperm nucleus, enters the egg in fertilization, it becomes clear that the only identical contribution from the two parents to their child is 1 set of chromosomes from each.

This very important fact already points up the paramount significance of the chromosomes. Consideration of another fact strongly underscores their significance. We have, in passing, noted that (most fortunately for the student of heredity!) the individual chromosomes of a cell may differ in size and shape and that these differences are quite as constant in all the cells of a given organism as is chromosome number. Consider, as an

39

example, fertilization in an organism having a normal chromosome number of 8. Sperm and egg, therefore, contain 4 chromosomes each, every chromosome having a distinctive size and shape. Figure 13A shows the stage of fertilization in which the sperm and egg nuclei lie beside one another. We see that the 2 nuclei contain identical complements of chromosomes; there

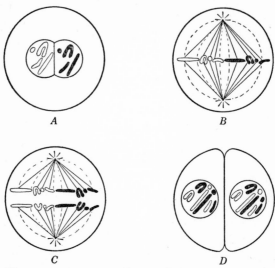

A   B

C   D

FIG. 13. The same stages as in Fig. 12, but assuming twice the normal number of chromosomes (8 here, only 4 in Fig. 12), and the 4 identical chromosomes contained in the female and male nucleus, respectively, being of different, typical size and shape.

is a short rod, a long rod, a horseshoe-shaped element, and a round, dotlike chromosome, in each nucleus. This arrangement is, of course, what we expect, for the two parents must contribute the same set of chromosomes to their offspring. Division of the fertilized egg takes place in exactly the way we have previously followed (Fig. 13B-D). Each daughter cell now contains a *pair* of each kind of chromosome, one partner of each pair being derived from the mother, the other from the father. Every cell of the body of this organism will contain 4 *pairs* of chromosomes. This is the direct consequence of the visible differentness of the chromosomes (4 kinds in the example) and of the fact that the egg and sperm nuclei arrive at fertilization

40

with identical chromosome sets. Extensive study has demonstrated that all body cells of all organisms developed from fertilized eggs except the mature egg and sperm cells do contain 2 sets of chromosomes, 1 derived from the mother, 1 from the father. This fact explains why it is that chromosome numbers are even, not odd. Each individual chromosome of a set is distinct from the rest of the set and has a partner identical to it in the second set.

The reduction of the chromosomes in the maturation divisions

What, now, is the mechanism producing mature sex cells with only a single set of chromosomes from immature cells containing the normal, duplex chromosome equipment typical of cells? From the facts discussed up to this point we can almost predict the answer to this problem, although an enormous amount of painstaking work was actually needed to seek out and convincingly demonstrate the solution. Each sex cell, male or female, passes through a maturation period before it is ready for the events of fertilization. During the maturing period, 2 peculiar and unique cell divisions occur, in course of which the original 2 sets of chromosomes are reduced to but 1 per cell. These maturation divisions are accordingly called *reduction divisions,* and the mature sex cells can be most properly called reduced sex cells. "Reduced" here means, obviously, that the cell contains a reduced number of chromosomes, half the normal number and specifically 1 set of chromosomes, including 1 chromosome of each type characteristic of the organism.

Since there are 2 maturation divisions, 4 mature sex cells with a reduced or half-normal number of chromosomes will be formed from each immature sex cell with a normal chromosome number. There is but little difference—little in essentials, although it may seem at first sight considerable—between egg and sperm cells in these 2 divisions. We have seen that the egg is usually filled with yolk and other substances needed for development of the embryo. Should the immature but yolk-laden egg cell divide into 4 equal cells, all these stored materials, assembled during a long growth phase, would be partitioned into quarter lots. Nature rarely makes such mistakes. The integrity of the storehouse is ensured by making the 2 egg maturation divisions

41

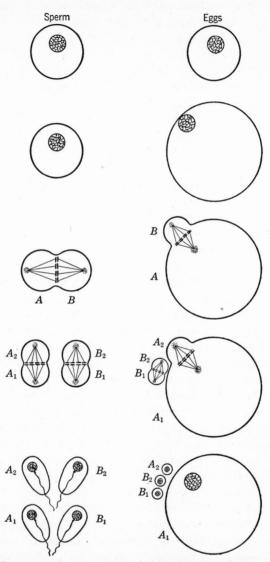

Fig. 14. Diagrammatic comparison of the maturation divisions in sperm cells (*left*) and eggs (*right*). The egg produces in 2 divisions 1 large mature egg cell and 3 tiny polar bodies that degenerate. The sperm cell divides into 4 viable mature sperm cells that transform into 4 spermatozoa (= sperm).

42

grossly unequal. The division figure with its rays and fibers is located near the surface of the large egg, with the result that cytoplasmic division separates a nearly intact egg from, at the opposite pole of the figure, a very tiny cell with a minimal amount of cytoplasm (see Fig. 14, right). A second, similar division follows, both the large egg and the very small cell dividing. Four cells are thus formed, but 1 of them retains substantially the whole of the stored yolk and other materials essential to development, while the other 3—called *polar bodies* (an established if inappropriate name bestowed on them before their real nature became known)—are minuscule and soon die or disappear. The immature male or sperm cell, in contrast, contains no yolk and is a small cell of standard form (Fig. 14, left). Its 2 maturation divisions are equal, and all 4 of the resulting cells become, by the transformation already described, motile sperm. Figure 14 compares these external features of the maturation divisions in egg and sperm.

These so-called "external" differences between male and female sex cells are rather insignificant so far as heredity is concerned; they may, indeed, be entirely lacking, as in certain lower organisms. The essential feature of the reduction divisions is what their name implies, the halving of the chromosome number. The process for accomplishing this is identical in egg and sperm, as we should certainly anticipate, in view of the chromosomal identity of egg and sperm in fertilization. And precisely this process is the salient one. It is an entirely minor matter that ¾ of the mature egg cells disappear as useless polar bodies, whereas all mature sperm cells are functional.

To follow chromosomal events during the reduction divisions we may return to the example of Fig. 13. There we had a basic chromosome number of 8, including 4 different kinds, each present as a pair, 1 partner of every pair coming from the mother and 1 from the father by way of the egg and sperm nuclei united in fertilization. Figure 13 depicts only the first 2 cells of the new organism, but it must be remembered that the chromosome picture in all later cells of the body will be exactly the same as in these two. So it will also be in the immature sex cells up to the time the maturation divisions begin. One of these cells is shown in Fig. 15A. After the chromosomes become visible in an immature sex cell a series of complicated changes and movements ensues, such as occur in no other type of cell but do take place in the immature sex cells of all plants and animals. We can omit

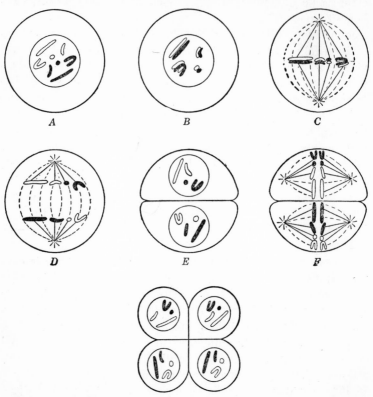

Fig. 15. A simplified representation of the maturation division of the sex cells. Chromosomes of maternal origin, white; of paternal, black. (*A*) Sex cell before maturation. (*B*) Pairing of homologous (parental) chromosomes into 4 closely associated pairs. (Normal number of chromosomes, 8.) (*C*) Equatorial plate of maturation division with 4 chromosome pairs (instead of 8 individual chromosomes). (*D*) Separation of whole chromosomes (instead of split halves in ordinary cell division), a maternal one going to one pole, the paternal one, in each group, to the other pole. (*E*) Each daughter nucleus contains a single set of chromosomes (reduced number: 4).
(*F*) Second maturation division. Below, the 4 mature sex cells.

a detailed account of these changes, fascinating though they are, and focus our attention on the basic facts. The essential point is that these processes join the pairs of like chromosomes along their entire length into a twin pair of chromosomes. Each pair

44

of equivalent or, to use the technical term, *homologous,* chromosomes consists, as we already know, of 1 chromosome of maternal origin (white in the figure) and 1 of paternal origin (black in the figure).

At this juncture the reader may see a difficulty. It was claimed that the chromosomes in the sex cells of this organism are precisely the chromosomes contributed at fertilization by the parents of this particular individual. Yet between fertilization and the production of immature sex cells innumerable cell divisions have intervened. Moreover, during the resting stages between active divisions no chromosomes were visible in cell nuclei. Have the original chromosomes actually survived all these resting and dividing periods? I can confidently answer: They have. Proof of this statement has been hard to come by, but it is available. The chromosomes maintain their individuality, intact through the whole series of cell divisions up to the immature sex cells, and, further, through the generations of children, grandchildren, great-grandchildren, and on and on.

In the reduction division process, after the homologous chromosomes have paired (Fig. 15B), a typical division figure is formed. But here 4 pairs of closely approximated chromosomes align themselves at the cell equator (Fig. 15C), in contrast to the 8 single chromosomes that line up in an ordinary division. In a usual cell division each of the 8 chromosomes duplicates itself and 1 daughter chromosome migrates to each of the cell poles. Not so in the reduction division. Here 1 member of each homologous pair moves to each pole, a black chromosome to the upper pole (Fig. 15D), a white chromosome to the lower pole or vice versa. Each daughter cell therefore receives only 1 representative of each homologous pair of each chromosome type. The chromosome number has been halved, and each cell formed receives a single set, albeit a complete set, of chromosomes (Fig. 15E).

It might be expected that the cells would now be ready to mature as they are, reduction having been accomplished. But instead, a second maturation division occurs. This, unlike the first maturation division, is a quite ordinary cell division, in which each chromosome splits longitudinally (Fig. 15F) and each daughter nucleus receives one of the split halves of the daughters of every chromosome in the parent cell. The reader may

45

justly wonder why this second division takes place. An explanation would require us to investigate details omitted here because of their complexity. Still a hint, to be elaborated in a later chapter, may be given: Due to certain events at the very beginning of the process, the first division may not completely separate the "black" and "white" chromosomes of a homologous pair from one another; the second division then achieves this separation and thus serves as a safety factor ensuring complete separation of homologous chromosomes. For our present discussion of the most important facts of genetics we can, indeed, neglect the second division. Hereafter, we shall speak of "the" reduction division, assuming that the first division does completely separate homologous partners in each chromosome pair, just as illustrated.

In "the" reduction division we saw that, for any single pair of chromosomes, a chromosome of maternal origin united with 1 of paternal origin, and then 1 of the pair went into one daughter cell and the second moved into the other daughter cell. Our example, however, included 4 pairs of chromosomes. A variety of patterns of separation of the whole complement of pairs can be conceived. It might be expected, for example, that all 4 maternal (white) chromosomes will go to one cell pole and all 4 paternal (black) chromosomes will end up at the other pole. But it is also thinkable that simple chance determines to which pole a black or a white chromosome moves at the times of separation of partners, namely, that a particular chromosome will go to the pole which happens to be nearest it as it lies on the equatorial plate. One possibility is that all the black chromosomes will go to one pole, all white to the other; or, by chance, 3 blacks and 1 white may go to one pole, 3 whites and 1 black to the other; all other possibilities can be readily visualized. Since each pair can assume 2 orientations—white up and black down, black up and white down—and since 4 pairs are present, 8 different arrangements of the 4 pairs on the division figure are possible and 16 types of daughter cells can be formed, differing with respect to which individual white and black chromosomes each receives. Figure 16 shows these 8 different kinds of division figures and the 16 types of daughter cells resulting, if chance alone controls the position of each chromosome pair in the spindle, quite independently of every other pair. Painstaking study of suitable material in which individual chromosomes could

46

be identified and followed has clearly established that this is the real situation. Maternal and paternal chromosomes are distributed only according to chance during reduction division; at

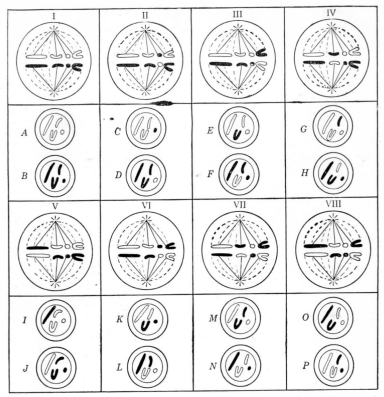

FIG. 16. Reduction division with 4 pairs of chromosomes, those of maternal origin white, of paternal black. Chance decides which of the partners of a pair is aligned to move to one or the other pole, each pair of chromosomes acting independently. Thus 8 different types of equatorial plates are possible, I–VIII, and after the maturation division 16 different types of mature sex cells are possible (A–P), different in regard to their combinations of "black" and "white" chromosomes.

the same time, each daughter cell receives a full set of chromosomes, including 1 and only 1 of each kind typical for the given organism.

On one occasion when the author presented these facts in a popular lecture, a listener arose at discussion time to ask: "This

47

is all very interesting and very nice, but who has ever seen a chromosome?" Well, chromosomes were seen for the first time only about 75 years ago, and the labor of a generation of assiduous workers went into unraveling the facts of cell division, fertilization, and reduction division, which have here been summarized in a few pages. Nowadays every beginning biology student observes the major features of these processes. That this is not so very difficult can be seen from a few photographs of stained chromosomes, reproduced as Fig. 17.

The individuality of the chromosomes

Just here, near the end of our consideration of the elementary facts of chromosomal behavior, we need to reemphasize a point made previously. We have studied chromosomes of the sex cells and chromosomes of the body cells, chromosomes of parents and chromosomes of their offspring, and we have taken it for granted that these were always the same chromosomes, both within one organism and in its parents and descendants. Let us examine the meaning of this principle more closely. Take, as an example, man. At fertilization egg and sperm each contribute 24 chromosomes to the new individual. The fertilized egg divides, and each daughter cell receives the normal number of 48 chromosomes. These 2 cells divide again and again, innumerable times, as the embryo, the infant, the child grow, until the adult, with his billions of cells, is formed. Then 20 years or so after the parental sex cells began this story, the succedent generation is ready to reproduce. Its immature sex cells contain the same 48 chromosomes as were present in the nuclei of sex cells of the parents and, clearly, of the grandparents and of more and more remote ancestors. The children and grandchildren and so on will repeat the pattern. Through all the generations of cells and individuals the chromosomes remain the same. Incredible as this may sound, it is in principle precisely the same as saying that man procreates man, flies produce flies, and corn yields nothing but corn. Now, obviously, this constancy of the chromosomes (sometimes called the law of chromosome individuality) cannot mean that the *substance* of the chromosomes remains unchanged. The mass of the chromosomes of a billion cells is, at best, a billion times the mass of the chromosomes of a fertilized egg. So far as quantity is concerned, the substance of chromo-

48

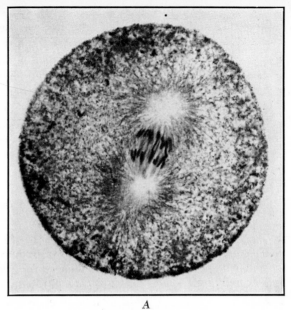

A

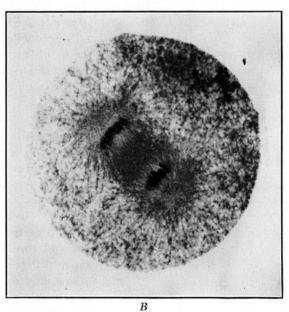

B

Fig. 17. Photomicrographs of some types of chromosomes. (A, B) Chromosomes in the dividing sea-urchin egg; (A) Daughter chromosomes just moving apart, (B) arrived at the spindle poles.

49

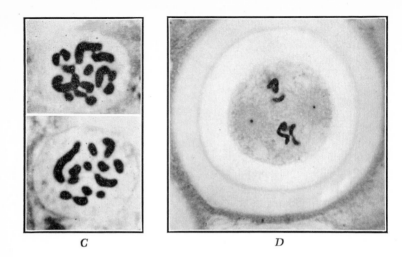

C   D

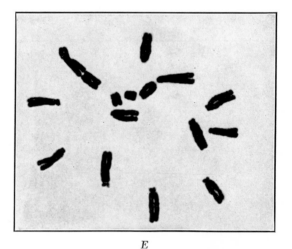

E

Fɪɢ. 17 (*Continued*). Photomicrographs of chromosomes. (*C*) Chromosomes of different size in female (*top*) and male (*bottom*) cells of a bug. The large chromosomes (2 in the female, 1 in the male cell) are the sex chromosomes (see below). (*D*) The 4 large chromosomes (partly foreshortened in the photo) in the first division of the egg of a roundworm. The 2 maternal and paternal chromosomes, respectively (see Fig. 12), are still lying apart. (*E*) The pairwise united homologous chromosomes before the maturation divisions of a pollen grain, 15 pairs of chromosomes. (Original photographs by Belar, Levan, Wilson, author.)

somes should double between each 2 cell divisions. The *quality* of the chromosomal substance, however, persists unchanged, and the law of individuality refers only to quality. We must conclude the chromosome has an intimate structure, an organization, with the capacity for self-propagation, for duplicating itself, for, to express it still another way, creating its own exact likeness at the time of cell division. Precisely because they are self-duplicating structures, the chromosomes remain qualitatively the same throughout all the generations of cells and organisms. This is their most important property, though its interpretation in exact physical and chemical terms is not yet possible. In a later chapter I shall have to qualify these statements and to show that sometimes changes in the chromosomes do occur.

Body cells, sex cells, and the continuity of the germ plasm

In the preceding discussion a distinction between body cells and sex cells has appeared repeatedly. A skin cell, muscle cell, or potential nerve cell divides many times as the organism develops. Some of these body cells retain their capacity for division as long as the organism lives; others, like the nerve cells, stop dividing at certain developmental stages and remain unchanged after achieving their final form and number. Ultimately, all these body cells are used up; they grow old and die just as does the individual. Is this true also of the sex cells? Unfertilized eggs, and sperm cells that find no egg cells, certainly die. The fertilized egg, however, continues to divide, thus linking one generation to the next. Though all other cells eventually perish, the sex cells alone survive the individual by giving rise to a new individual. Were every egg and every sperm to enter into fertilization, as is theoretically possible but almost never achieved, every sex cell would in a sense survive in its descendants.

It is not really quite accurate to say that sex cells *alone* are capable of such continuity and persistence. For, under certain conditions, body cells can do the same. Everyone is aware that among plants a collection of body cells, in the form of a cutting, reproduce the organism indefinitely, that there are plants, like the banana tree, which have been cultivated for thousands of years without sexual reproduction. Certain kinds of lower animals, as polyps, sponges, and worms, can similarly be cut into pieces, each fragment subsequently growing into a complete ani-

51

mal; also, some animals can reproduce *asexually*—i.e., without production of sex cells—by simply dividing into two, or by forming buds, offshoots that later become independent individuals. Body cells may thus retain, in some degree, their potentiality for indefinitely continued division. This potentiality is most dramatically exhibited by cells isolated from the body and grown, by special techniques, in an artificial medium in a test tube. In such a situation they can continue dividing, perhaps indefinitely. For example, chicken cells have been kept alive and actively dividing for a time span in which dozens of generations of fowl could have come and gone.

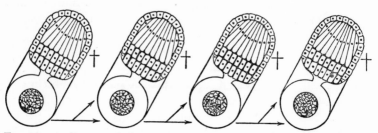

Fig. 18. A diagram of the continuity of the germ plasm. (*Below*) The "immortal" line of the sex cells, (*above*) the "mortal" body cells.

Aside from these special cases, it is a general rule that the prime difference between sex cells and body cells is this: Body cells are mortal whereas sex cells are virtually immortal. By "immortal" is meant that these cells do not die but, by division, give rise to a new organism, whose body cells are bound to die, but whose sex cells, stemming like the body cells from the parental sex cells, will produce the next generation. One can say, then, that a straight line, a "thread of life," joints the sex cells of all the generations, whereas the death-limited body cells are mere blind branches from the main line. Figure 18 represents this concept, the so-called principle of *continuity of the germ plasm*. Here the organism is represented as a group of various kinds of cells to which is attached an egg cell (sperm and fertilization are omitted for the sake of simplicity). The body dies (indicated by +), but the egg cell of the first generation is connected by a straight line to the egg of the next, whose body is again a death-fated side branch, whereas the egg carries the line to a third generation, etc.

52

It is rather remarkable that, at least in the animal kingdom, this general idea of the continuity of germ plasm can actually be observed in some cases (such demonstration is usually but not completely lacking in plants). We might suppose that during the development of any animal continuous cell division, initiated by the fertilized egg, produces a large number of equivalent

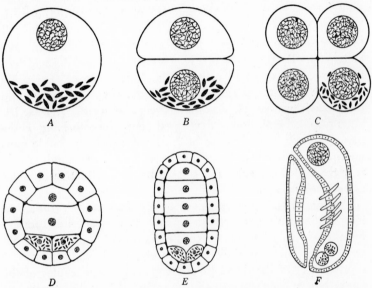

FIG. 19. A diagram of the germ track: The sex cells, characterized by the black dots in their cytoplasm, are separated already in the first divisions of the egg and remain apart (2 primary sex cells) during the development of the organism, shown in different schematic stages.

cells, some of which become body cells of a variety of types, while others form sex cells. In many cases it can be shown that the actual process is rather different: The future sex cells are set aside during the earliest stages of development, are, so to speak, kept in reserve against their future use. In some animals the sex cells are separated, or begin to be segregated, as early as the first division of the fertilized egg. Figure 19 is a diagram showing how this important process takes place. In some cases special inclusions can be seen at definite positions in the proto-plasm of the fertilized egg cell (like the black granules in Fig. 19A). The portion of protoplasm marked by these granules will, in fact, later form part of the bodies of the sex cells of the new organism. After the first division all the special granules lie in 1 of the 2 resulting cells (Fig. 19B). It is possible to trace precisely the developmental fates of the descendants of each of these 2 cells and, from such studies, to assert that the upper cell in the figure, the one lacking granules, will give rise only to body cells, whereas the lower cells, which contain all these granules, will produce sex cells, as the outcome of its future divisions. In Fig. 19C we see that both cells have divided again; 3 of the cells now present contain none of the granules and can form body cells only. By the stage of Fig. 19D 16 cells have formed by 2 more divisions of the 4 cells of Fig. 19B. Two of the 16, the only cells with the granules, are the first sex cells; their subsequent divisions can yield nothing except sex cells. In Fig. 19E a many-celled embryo has developed (only the cells lying on one plane through its body have been drawn); distinguishable outer and inner cell layers of body cells have already appeared. At the rear the first 2 sex cells, identifiable by the distinctive granules, are still to be seen.

Finally, in the embryo (seen in section) of Fig. 19F, skin, intestinal, muscle, and nerve cells have differentiated and formed primitive organs. The 2 sex cells remain readily distinguishable. Only much later will they divide to give the immature eggs (or sperm cells) of the developing sex glands. In examples of this kind, the sex cells can actually be followed in a direct and continuous series from generation to generation; they travel, so to speak, along what is sometimes termed a germ track.

With this we conclude our study of the basic facts concerning the sex cells and their chromosomes, facts that must be mastered if one wishes to understand heredity. The sex cells—called *gametes* when their maleness or femaleness is irrelevant—loom large in the following inquiry into heredity, and we shall often have need to refer back to this chapter.

Elementary Mendelism

From the preceding chapters we have gained some insight into the nature of the visible inheritable characteristics of living organisms and some acquaintance with the sex cells, which, we have seen, must contain whatever is essential for reproducing hereditary traits of parents in their offspring. Now we must discover the relations between these two sets of facts, must trace inheritable attributes from parents to progeny and determine just how the transmission is effected.

Hybridization as a means to the study of heredity

The proper and necessary first step in any inquiry is to think out a way to find the answers to our questions. Let us, therefore, consider possible approaches. As a first possibility, we may take two parents who are completely alike in every single hereditary feature and who consequently will each transmit exactly the same inheritable features to their children. Obviously enough, the offspring will be identical to both parents in all these traits, for this is the meaning of the words "hereditary characters." Clearly, no additional information can be obtained from such a mating. As a second attempt, then, let us restrict the choice of traits somewhat and assume, for example, that the parents are a pair of "full-blooded" Negroes and that we are interested in learning how the hereditary features which characterize what we call a Negro are transmitted. The children will, of course, be Negroes, and the only knowledge we gain is that the group of characters followed—skin color, hair form, nose shape, etc.—is inheritable. We see that we must proceed differently if we are to discover the mechanism of heredity.

What we must do is to pair genetically *different* individuals, say, a Negro and a Caucasian, and observe how their inheritable traits behave both in the direct offspring and in later generations. Right here the naïve observer is almost certain to make a profound mistake. He will look at the offspring as whole individuals, conclude that they exhibit a mixture of the parental sets of characters, and simply mark them down as "mulattoes" or "half-bloods." In the same way, when he sees children from the marriage of a so-called "mulatto" to a full Negro, he will refer to them as "three-quarter Negro"; the children of a "mulatto" married to a Caucasian he will call "one-quarter Negroes" or "quadroons." This manner of description gives us no insight whatever into the problem of how the presumed Negroid and Caucasoid traits are inherited. Nothing emerges except a word, "blood-mixture," and this term is much better forgotten, for, as we shall soon see, nothing is mixed, and blood has nothing whatsoever to do with hereditary transmission. From the discussion in the first chapter it should already be clear where lies the primary fallacy of this erring approach. Rather than consider the total impression made by a large number of individual features in the parents and their progeny, we must confine ourselves to single inheritable characters—skin color alone, for example, or hair form—and follow this by itself through the several generations of *hybrids.*

The English word "bastard" and its Greek equivalent "hybrid" (from *hybris,* sin) have acquired tainted connotations. The biologist, however, does not moralize. In his usage, the offspring of any mating between two genetically different individuals is a *hybrid* or *cross,* and the mating is a *hybridization* or *crossing.* The mule is a hybrid, from the crossing of horse and ass; the "mulatto" is a hybrid, from the marriage of a Negro and a Caucasian; the mating of a redhead and brunette is also a hybridization, and their children are hybrids in just the same sense; so, too, are the progeny from the crossing of two lines of beans, which differ hereditarily in regard to a small fraction of seed size.

Here, then, we have what seems to be a sound method for accomplishing our aim of understanding hereditary transmission. Historically, it was precisely this procedure of concentrating attention on a single hereditary difference, a single pair of inheritable characters, and the results, for this pair, of hybridization that led to the great discovery known as Mendel's laws of heredity.

Mendel's discovery

About the middle of the nineteenth century the Augustine monk Gregor Mendel began experiments in crossing peas, continuing them over the years in a tiny garden plot at the King's monastery in Bruenn, Austria (now Brno, Czechoslovakia). Combining the art of careful experimentation, founded on clear conceptions of what he wanted to do, with the capacity for incisive analysis of the results, his genius succeeded in discovering those natural laws which have made his name known the world over. In 1865 his results, which were to become the foundations of the new science of genetics, were published as a short paper in the reports of a local natural history society. Nobody took any notice whatsoever of them. For 35 years these pages, now celebrated as a model of concentrated reporting of experiments and keen analysis, rested in obscurity. The time, years before the discovery of the mechanism of cell division, chromosomes, and the real process of fertilization, was not yet ripe for the paper in which the gist of these later discoveries was quietly anticipated. Not until 1900, long after Mendel's death, were his laws rediscovered by Correns in Germany, De Vries in Holland, and Tschermak in Austria, and was Mendel's original work brought to world attention. The fundamental importance of "Mendelism" was then quickly recognized. "Mendelism" and "to Mendelize" (to inherit according to Mendel's laws) became household words of the biologist.

We shall begin our study of Mendel's laws of heredity not with his own original material, garden peas, but with another experiment, which is even easier to understand. We make a cross (as in Fig. 20) between two varieties of the common four-o'clock (*Mirabilis jalapa*), the strains being identical except for flower color, one having red, the other white flowers. The offspring, irrespective of which variety was used as mother and which as father (seed plant and pollen plant), invariably have flowers of intermediate color, a light, pinkish red. To the uninstructed it appears that the parental characters have been commingled. But we should not make this error, for we have already

learned that external appearance does not tell us what the underlying hereditary constitution is. With due caution, therefore, we
note only that the phenotype of the hybrid is intermediate between the parental phenotypes. The propriety of this caution
immediately becomes evident when we breed a *second hybrid
generation,* that is, a second generation produced by self-pol-

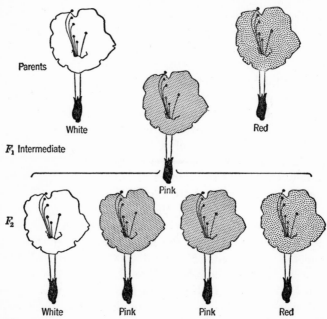

FIG. 20. Cross between a red- and white-flowering four-o'clock (*Mirabilis
jalapa*): parents, F_1, and F_2. F_1 intermediate, F_2 segregation 1 : 2 : 1.

linating the first (in plants with separate sexes and in animals
the second hybrid generation would be produced by brother-
sister mating). In the second hybrid generation, we see the
apparently mixed parental characters clearly reappearing and
segregating from one another. Our flower bed now contains
red-flowered and white-flowered four-o'clocks, indistinguishable
from the original parental varieties, as well as pink-flowered
plants identical with the first hybrid generation. The question
arises: Are the white and red plants *segregating* in this second
hybrid generation really pure? Have all traces of the foregoing
generation disappeared? In other words, will they hereafter be

58

able to produce only their kind? For an answer we must grow a third generation, bred from whites alone and from reds alone. We find that the whites do indeed produce only white-flowered plants, and the reds do have only red-flowered progeny, just as in the two original varieties; moreover, however long we breed them, whites produce only whites, reds nothing but reds. In other words, the true-breeding white and, similarly, the red, have cleanly segregated in the second hybrid generation; from the apparent mixture of the first generation the original parental types have emerged unchanged.

The second generation, however, does include some light reds, indistinguishable from the first generation hybrids. These we proceed to test by producing a third generation through self-pollination or brother-sister matings. What do we find? The third generation repeats exactly the results of the second hybrid generation: Reds, whites, and light reds appear. Once more we select and breed from the white-flowered plants, and in the same way from the reds; each produces only its own color type in succeeding generations. As the expression goes, they *breed true*. But the light reds, when selfed (self-pollinated), reproduce again the results of the first- and second-hybrid-generation light reds, yielding all three colors. Thus we find that the offspring of light red hybrids are true-breeding whites, true-breeding reds, and segregating light red hybrids.

The elementary Mendelian ratio and the purity of the gametes

Now let us go back to the plot of second-generation plants, red, white, and light red, and count the number of each type, as Mendel was the first to do in a breeding experiment. Provided that the bed is large, with many plants, the result is a very orderly one. Almost exactly one-fourth of the four-o'clocks have white flowers; another one-fourth, red blooms; and the remaining two-fourths, light red blossoms. However often we may repeat the experiment, we shall always find the numerical relations to be the same; indeed, the larger the total number of plants counted, the more closely will this proportion be approached. If we grow a third generation from the second-generation light reds, the segregation—which we may call a *Mendelian segregation*—again approximates one-quarter true-

59

breeding whites, one-quarter true-breeding reds, and two-quarters hybrid light reds. Precisely these numbers, the ratio of 1 : 2 : 1, led Mendel's incisive mind to the explanation for what actually happens in heredity.

Mendel's argument ran somewhat as follows: The organism is the result of the union of the female and male sex cells in fertilization. (Remember that the actual events in fertilization, which we studied in the previous chapter, were wholly unknown in Mendel's time!) The sex cells, therefore, must contain something responsible for the production of a hereditary character—in our example, flower color. This something may be called a hereditary *factor,* though nowadays the term *gene* is generally applied. If an organism is true-breeding for a character —red or white color in the four-o'clocks—the sex cells of both parents must have contained the same hereditary factor or gene. In the white variety, both the egg from the maternal plant and the pollen from the paternal plant must have carried the gene for producing white color (which we may, for brevity, call the "white gene," though it must be emphasized that it is the character produced, not the gene, which is actually, in the example, white). Similarly in the red variety. The hybrid, clearly, must have received a red gene from one parent and a white gene from the other. The light red phenotype thus seems to indicate that the combined action of the red and the white genes together in the same plant produces a compromise result, the pinkish color. We saw, further, that among the offspring of this hybrid true-breeding reds and whites again appear. If white (or red) is the result of both parents' contributing a white (or red) gene, it follows that both sexes of the hybrid produced some sex cells carrying only the white gene and some carrying only the red gene. The light red hybrid, in other words, does not form sex cells or gametes in which white and red are mixed but produces only sex cells containing either the red or the white gene; the gametes of the hybrid are *pure* for one or the other gene. This law of the *purity of gametes* was Mendel's first great discovery and is one of the cornerstones of genetics. Only one additional hypothesis was needed to explain the whole situation: When the hybrid forms sex cells, chance determines which sex cells receive the gene for red and which gametes the gene for white. Because of the operation of chance, half of the gametes will, on the average, receive the red factor; and half, the white factor.

The laws of the purity of gametes and of the chance distribution of a pair of genes among the gametes of the hybrid simply and convincingly explained both segregation and its numerical ratio. (For brevity, we may speak, as we have above of "white genes" and "red genes," of "white gametes" and "red gametes" instead of "sex cells carrying the factor producing red [or white] color.") The true-breeding varieties produced only red gametes or only white gametes; union of red with red in fertilization can result in a red-flowered plant only; white with white, only in a white-flowered plant. The hybrid between the two receives red from one parent, white from the other, and is genetically red-white. Since the hybrid's gametes must be pure, half of its sex cells are red, half are white (remember that these labels are a convenient but not precisely accurate shorthand). This is true for the female hybrid and male hybrid alike. In the breeding of a second generation from the hybrid, 2 types of eggs are available for fertilization, red and white in equal numbers, along with 2 types of pollen, red and white in equal numbers. If both types of pollen and both types of eggs have the same chance for uniting in fertilization, 4 types of fertilizations will occur in equal numbers:

1. Red egg cell fertilized by red pollen.
2. Red egg cell fertilized by white pollen.
3. White egg cell fertilized by red pollen.
4. White egg cell fertilized by white pollen.

The first obviously gives the one-fourth pure, true-breeding reds, for no white is present. Number 4 accounts for the one-fourth true-breeding whites. Numbers 2 and 3 represent the two-fourths of the second generation plants which are light red, hybrids for white and red; these will, in turn, form pure red and white gametes. In this way both the segregation of the second hybrid generation, in contrast to the uniformity of the first generation, and its numerical ratio of types are explained by Mendel's three rules of purity of gametes, production of gametes in equal numbers with respect to a single pair of genes, and their combination in fertilization according to chance. This, in its elegant simplicity, is the essence of Mendelism; from these elementary principles, since confirmed in thousands of examples, all the rest of the science of heredity has been derived, built up, or expanded.

Dominance and the classic ratio

We began this account of Mendel's basic laws by remarking that our example is a little simpler than that studied by Mendel himself in his peas. The difference between the two cases is really of little importance. Genetically, both are alike. The deviation lies only in the outward appearance, the phenotype of the hybrid. In the four-o'clock, the characters of the parents were seemingly mixed; the phenotype of the hybrid was intermediate between those of its parents. In a great many hybrids the situation is otherwise, and it happened that Mendel's pea characters fell into this second category of effect. In these cases the gene derived from one parent acts so strongly in the formation of the character in question as to cover up completely the action of the gene from the other parent. The phenotype of the hybrid consequently resembles exactly that of the single parent supplying the more effective gene, what Mendel called the *dominant* gene. The opposing gene, the action of which is not visible in the hybrid, is called the *recessive* factor. Thus, when Mendel crossed a line of peas with yellow seeds to one with green seeds, yellow was dominant, and the hybrid failed to exhibit any external effect of the green parent. Similarly, purple flower color in peas turned out to be dominant over white. Another investigator found that, in the cross of a variety of garden snail with plain yellow shell to one with black bands, the hybrid is plain yellow; yellow is dominant to banded (Fig. 21). Innumerable examples could be cited of pairs of hereditary characters in which one is dominant to the other, but in a great many other cases the phenotype of the hybrid is intermediate between those of its parents. There is no rule determining which of the two conditions will exist in any particular case. The naïve person, observing dominant *behavior*, tends to make the completely unwarranted assumption that the more intelligent, or stronger-willed, or more passionate parent will have the dominant hereditary trait. There is no truth in such ideas. Dominance and recessiveness are the result of the way the respective genes react during development. By experimental manipula-

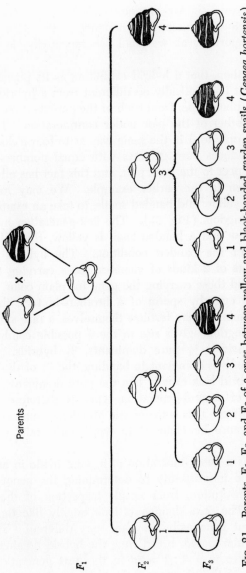

FIG. 21. Parents, F₁, F₂, and F₃ of a cross between yellow and black-banded garden snails (*Cepaea hortensis*), banded being recessive, F₂ segregation 3 : 1.

tion of the conditions of development, for example, its rate, one can change a dominant action into a recessive one or into some step in between. So far as elementary genetic theory is concerned, therefore, dominance is a minor matter, although it is extremely important, as we shall see repeatedly, in terms of phenotypes.

We learn, then, that a hybrid exhibiting as its phenotype the dominant trait is genetically no different from a hybrid with an intermediate phenotype; from each of the parents it receives one gene or the other of the pair under consideration. The Mendelian laws apply to it in the same way as to four-o'clock flower color. It produces pure gametes with equal numbers of each type with respect to the gene pair, and this fact has all the consequences seen in the earlier example. We may follow the results in the yellow and banded snails, to take an example from the animal kingdom (Fig. 21). The first-generation hybrid between a yellow and a banded snail is yellow, this color being dominant over the banded condition. The hybrids produce equal numbers of 2 kinds of gametes, those carrying the gene for banded and those carrying the gene for plain color. Fertilization of the eggs by sperm of a brother—in fact, these hermaphroditic animals may fertilize themselves, a rare situation in the animal kingdom—gives rise to the 4 possible combinations: ¼ pure recessives, ¼ pure dominants, ²⁄₄ hybrids. Because absence of bands is dominant to banding, the ²⁄₄ of the progeny which are hybrid look exactly like the pure dominants, and the visible ratio of second-generation types is therefore 3 dominant : 1 recessive. This is the classic Mendelian ratio as Mendel stated it, because he chanced to work with traits exhibiting dominance.

This ratio is a good illustration of a point made in an earlier discussion: the impossibility of determining the genotype, the hereditary constitution, from simple inspection of the phenotype alone. The pure dominants look exactly like the hybrid dominants, but genetically they are very different. The pure dominants, when mated, breed true; the hybrid dominants produce both types in a 3 : 1 ratio in the next generation. The deceptiveness of the phenotype, the outward dress, in masking various genotypes is thus disclosed by the breeding experiment or, in technical terms, by making a progeny test. We may

64

now look back at the pedigree of bleeder's disease, which we studied previously (Fig. 1). There we saw that normal, non-bleeder women, daughters of a bleeder, could transmit the condition to some of their offspring, despite their own phenotypes. It is clear that such women had both a dominant gene for normalcy and a recessive for bleeding and could therefore convey the recessive and unhappy trait to their descendants in a very definite way (which we shall soon analyze in detail). These examples, and thousands of similar ones, demonstrate also that, where dominance is involved, recessives segregating out of hybrids must always be true-breeding. This is an important conclusion both for genetic theory and for practical breeding and understanding of human heredity.

Nomenclature

Our study of Mendelism has reached the point where it will be convenient to introduce some of the terms, derived from Greek and Latin roots, which geneticists use for convenience and the facilitating of international understanding. Chromosome, gene or hereditary factor, dominant, recessive, phenotype, and genotype have already been introduced. A pair of genes showing Mendelian segregation in a 1 : 2 : 1 ratio after crossing (or 3 : 1 if dominance is involved) is called a pair of *alleles* (al·leles'; from the Greek word *allelos,* meaning one or the other). If an individual contains a pair of identical alleles, either the 2 dominants or the 2 recessives, and is therefore "pure" or "true-breeding" for the character controlled by the gene, that individual is said to be *homozygous* (ho'mo·zy'gous; the Greek root *homo,* meaning equal, plus *zygein,* meaning to unite), for equal or like genes have joined by way of fertilization to produce the *homozygote* (ho'mo·zy'gote). If unlike genes, a dominant and its recessive allele, unite (genes of a hybrid, we have called them so far), we speak of the individual as genetically *heterozygous* (het'er·o·zy'gous; *heteros* = different), for 2 different alleles have come together in the fertilization that produced the hybrid. The Mendelian segregation thus yields ¼ homozygous dominants, ¾ heterozygous dominants (or intermediates), and ¼ homozygous recessives. Visible recessives must always be homozygous. The hybrid snails were heterozygous for yellow and banded, with a dominance of yellow; the light red four-o'clocks were heterozygous for red and white. In what follows we shall also use the abbreviation P for the original parents (= parental generation) in a pedigree, F_1 (= first filial generation) for the first hybrid generation, F_2 for the second, F_3 for the third, etc. So one may write: The F_1 of a simple Mendelian cross is uniform; segregation occurs in the F_2. These few technical terms will suffice for much of the discussion to come.

Universality of Mendel's laws and application to man

Probably the next question the reader who has grasped the foregoing discussion will ask is this: Do these laws of Mendel have general validity? Do all hereditary traits show only this type of heredity; do they always Mendelize after crossing? First, we must be quite clear as to what is meant by "Mendelize." Thus far we have studied only the most elementary case. Actually, as we shall shortly see, much more complicated situations exist; but they will turn out, after all is said, to be variations on the same theme, so that the apparently most aberrant details will be derivable from the basic facts already presented. "To Mendelize" therefore has a broader meaning than merely following the simple rules of the classic experiment; it includes all the more or less complicated behavior of the genetic elements which can be derived from the simple case. In this sense, we can safely say that all the inheritable characteristics studied in plants and animals including man do Mendelize after crossing. This is true for such diverse attributes as color of flowers, skin, hair, eyes, leaves; form and size of the whole body or any of its parts; form of hair, whether straight, curled, woolly, Angora, long, short; shape and other detailed features of ears, nose, teeth, mouth; biochemical properties, such as ability or inability to synthesize certain vitamins; physiological characteristics, such as susceptibility to disease and infections, be it rust in wheat, plant lice in grapes, or cancer in mammals; pathological conditions, as short and curved legs, split nose, harelip, clubfoot, winglessness, duplication or abortion of organs, in all kinds of organisms; and, finally, psychological traits, whether instincts in animals or talent in man. Volumes could be filled with the enumeration of known Mendelizing traits of man, cattle, horses, mice, rats, guinea pigs, fowl, moths, beetles, wasps, flies, snails, plants of every description, and even Infusoria, bacteria, and viruses. There is a single species of fly, which we shall encounter repeatedly, for which almost a thousand Mendelizing characters are known; in man, as well, the catalogue is already long. Yet all these inheritable traits, whenever they can be followed in a breeding experiment, have been seen to Mendelize.

Staying, for the moment, within the limits of the most elementary facts of Mendelism, we may trace a few consequences of the rules demonstrated thus far. In doing so I propose to use examples from human heredity. People generally are most interested in people, however much the geneticist may be attracted to the guinea pigs, flies, maize plants, or molds which he can breed in large numbers, mate at will, treat with chemicals or radiations, and manipulate in whatever way his questing mind elects. Human traits can be studied, on the other hand, only in the actual family, whose members follow their own predilections in mate selection. In favorable cases human ancestry may be followed for a few generations, but frequently only secondhand information is available. Man is a long-lived organism, and hereditary traits often appear only in the later years; they are then many times unknown to other members of a family group. Man leaves only a few offspring, and the large numbers of pedigrees necessary for analysis are difficult to collect. For all these reasons man is not a particularly suitable material wherein to search for new genetical relations and laws. Yet there are certain advantages. For man is by far the best-known and best-studied organism in his normal anatomy; in his physiology, the functioning, including the chemical properties, of his body; in his pathology, the deviations from the norm, whether the result of disease or not; and in his psychology, his mental functions. Correspondingly, more, as well as more diversified, hereditary characters can be followed in man than in any other organism. Further, there exists a quite unexpected help to the genetic analysis of man, the fact of twinning, which can furnish reliable information that partly compensates for the impossibility of genetic experimentation.

In man (as well as in some other animals) a phenomenon occurs which is one aspect of twinning. Twin births (and triplets, quadruplets, and quintuplets) may result simply from the fertilization of more than one egg at a given time, as is the rule in, for example, dogs, cats, pigs, and mice. But some twins, called identical twins, are of an entirely different type. They occur when a single egg forms, exceptionally, more than one organism. For reasons not well understood, the embryo developing from a fertilized egg, in such cases, divides at some stage into two (rarely more) identical parts, each of which develops into a complete individual, one of the identical twins. Since both twins are derived from a single egg cell fertilized by a single sperm, they must be completely alike genetically, must carry exactly the same genes. Hence, if both exhibit a given character, this is presumably a hereditary feature. Everyone knows that identical twins do have the same sex, eye and hair color, facial conformation, all known to be hereditary. But assume that we do not know whether, for example, a particular type of cancer has a hereditary basis. If identical twins are born to a family having the disease, and if both, though possibly separated from birth, develop it at the same age, we can be almost certain that there is some hereditary disposition toward the ailment.

The Mendelian backcross

Now let us look at the general genetical situation in man. In experimenting with other organisms we can start a cross with a pair of homozygous individuals, say pure, homozygous, red- or white-flowered plants. In man such matings are relatively rare, save in the case of hereditary traits common to large numbers of individuals, as hair and eye colors, which are often homozygous. But for rare traits, like the presence of six fingers or toes on each limb, it is rather improbable that the individual had a father and a mother both of whom exhibited the trait, and therefore it is improbable that the individual will be homozygous. In the event of a dominant trait, like the presence of six fingers, called polydactyly (pol′y·dac′ty·ly; from Greek *polys*, meaning many, and *daktylos*, meaning finger), we can expect the polydactylous individual to be heterozygous for the polydactyl gene. As a rule he or she will marry a normal person, and the mating will be a hybridization. A mating of this type is called a *backcross*. We see that human matings will very often be backcrosses. What is the result of such a cross?

The outcome can be easily understood if we study backcrosses in yellow and banded snails. The F_1 of yellow crossed to banded, it will be remembered, was yellow, this being the dominant trait. Now a useful way to visualize the genetic constitution of the hybrid is to write the contribution of the two parents in the form of a fraction, indicating dominance by a capital initial letter:

$$F_1 = \frac{Plain}{banded}$$

A backcross of this hybrid could be made in two ways, either to the dominant or to the recessive parent. The backcross (we indicate a cross by the multiplication sign) between the F_1 hybrid and the dominant parent is, then,

$$\frac{Plain}{banded} \times \frac{Plain}{Plain}$$

As we know, the hybrid forms equal numbers of 2 kinds of gametes, those containing the recessive allele banded and those containing the dominant allele Plain; this we can at once read from the fraction. The dominant parent produces only 1 type of gametes, all containing Plain. The backcross thus permits only 2 kinds of fertilization, which occur in equal numbers:

(1) Plain fertilized by Plain
(2) banded fertilized by Plain

The result of the backcross is, then,

$$\frac{1}{2} \frac{Plain}{Plain} : \frac{1}{2} \frac{banded}{Plain}$$

or ½ homozygous Plain and ½ heterozygous Plain. The 2 groups cannot be distinguished phenotypically because Plain is dominant; this "dominant backcross" gives only 1 phenotype, the dominant. Genotypically, of course, half of the offspring are heterozygotes.

In the same way we can backcross the F_1 heterozygote to the recessive parent. Using the same notation, we can indicate this backcross as

$$\frac{Plain}{banded} \times \frac{banded}{banded}$$

Once more the hybrid forms 2 types of gametes; the pure recessive, only 1. The 2 possible types of fertilization yield as offspring

$$\frac{1}{2} \frac{\text{Plain}}{\text{banded}} : \frac{1}{2} \frac{\text{banded}}{\text{banded}}$$

or, equal numbers of the 2 phenotypes, Plain (genetically heterozygous) and banded. The recessive backcross produces equal numbers of the phenotypes of the two parents of the backcross, the dominant being heterozygous and the recessive homozygous. To the list of Mendelian F_2 ratios, $1 : 2 : 1$ and $3 : 1$, we can now add the backcross or RF_2 ratio $1 : 1$.

With this we are ready to follow the heredity of simple Mendelian human traits in a pedigree, where, we have seen, most matings will be backcrosses. Referring again to the example of dominant polydactyly, a polydactylous man or woman will generally be the child of a heterozygous polydactylous mother and a normal father (or one may exchange genotypes of the father and mother, for in simple Mendelian heredity it makes no difference which parent brings the gene in question into a mating). Half the children of this pair will, clearly, be polydactylous; the other half, normal. But before studying actual pedigrees another important fact should be made completely clear.

Ratios and probability

At this juncture a little more must be said about the $1 : 1$ and other Mendelian ratios. These ratios, we have seen, are based ultimately on the laws of probability, for it is chance which determines the occurrence of the possible types of fertilizations. Obviously, it follows that an approximation to the ideal equality of numbers in chance fertilization will become more likely as the number of fertilizations increases. The situation here is rather similar to what happens in casting dice. Imagine that we have two absolutely equal dice, one with the number five on all faces, one with five on three faces and six on the other three. If we throw these dice 100,000 times, we shall come very near to having two fives 50,000 times and one five and one six 50,000 times. But if we throw the dice only a few times, it may happen that we throw a string of double fives or of five and six. Out of ten throws we could have 5 : 5, 6 : 4, 7 : 3, 8 : 2, 9 : 1, or 10 : 0 of the two combinations, simply because of the small number of trials. In the same way, Mendelian ratios, based as they are on chance assortment, will be closer to the ideal expectation when the numbers are larger. In a single human family of four children segregating for polydactyly it is not surprising to find only one, none, three, or even all four showing the dominant trait. Four is too small a number to give the ideal 1 : 1 ratio in every case. But if we sum up the results in, say, 10,000 children of such families, we should then find very nearly 5000 polydactylous children. The mathematical statistician can tell us how many agreements and disagreements with the expected ratios are likely to occur with various numbers of progeny and how well actual counts will agree with theoretical expectation. In genetic research all numerical results are thus checked mathematically to decide whether they are "significant," whether they are close enough to expectation to accord with the genetic explanation. Even the beginner in genetics, though unable to make such statistical tests, should clearly understand that they are essential, that it would be wrong to judge the correctness of an interpretation, the goodness-of-fit of a result, from an individual case which appears to be in disagreement. A proper statistical test will show whether the disagreement is within the limits of expectation for the number of individuals used or whether the expectation has not been fulfilled.

Cases of human heredity

From this digression we may return to simple cases of human inheritance which, as a rule, will be of a backcross type. We can, however, imagine the following situation: The trait being studied occurs in a small population in a remote Alpine valley, where local marriages are the custom. In this situation a polydactylous woman—to use the same example—has a considerable chance of marrying a polydactylous man, because the population is closely inbred. If both individuals are heterozygous, the mating is the crossing of 2 F_1 hybrids to produce an F_2, and among the children a ratio of 3 abnormals to 1 normal is expected. In the ideal case, $\frac{1}{4}$ of the children will be homozygous dominants; these homozygous individuals, then, irre-

spective of their mates, can beget only polydactylous children.
Considering all these facts, we can construct a pedigree such as
could be found (and has been found times unnumbered) for
a family with a dominant hereditary trait. This pedigree (Fig.
22) also shows one way of presenting data on human heredity
intelligibly. The dominant allele is indicated in black, the

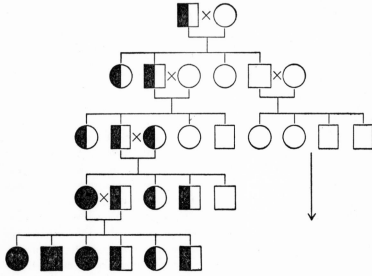

FIG. 22. Diagrammatic pedigree of a dominant trait in man. Squares =
males, circles = females; black is the dominant phenotype, black-white, the
heterozygote.

recessive in white, and the heterozygote is black-white. Each
individual's genotype thus can be represented. A circle stands
for a female, a square for a male. Each horizontal row represents a generation. Brackets above connect all the children of
1 parental couple; the multiplication sign indicates the mating;
the brackets below connect the two parents. In the first generation in the example a heterozygous man, phenotypically exhibiting the dominant trait, marries a normal, homozygous recessive woman. Of the 4 children, half are again heterozygous
abnormal, half recessive normal. A normal son (second row,
right) marries a normal woman. All their offspring (third row,
right) are genotypically and phenotypically normal; future gen-

erations (arrow) marrying normals will never again have polydactyly. One of the heterozygous sons of the original couple also weds a normal woman (second row, left). The 4 children of the third generation are again half heterozygous abnormal, half homozygous recessive normal. The heterozygous man of this third generation marries (third row, left) a woman also heterozygous and polydactyl (remember the Alpine valley). Their offspring (fourth row) are ¼ homozygous recessive normal, ²⁄₄ heterozygous polydactyl, and ¼ homozygous dominant polydactyl. Now the homozygous daughter in this fourth generation marries a heterozygous abnormal man; all their children (bottom row) are abnormal, half being homozygous, half heterozygous.

A great many important human abnormalities and disease predispositions belong to the class of recessive characters. A pedigree of such a character will look quite different from the foregoing one (Fig. 23). This time the dominant black individuals are normal, whereas in the first pedigree they were the abnormals. This difference must be kept in mind. Furthermore, only the homozygous recessives (white) can exhibit the anomaly; the heterozygotes (black-white) are phenotypically normal but carry a recessive allele for the abnormal condition. Individuals exhibiting the trait must here be homozygous. Children of an abnormal married to a normal are therefore always normal. If the normal parent was homozygous for the normal allele, all offspring will be heterozygous and normal. This is represented in Fig. 23 in the first two generations (top two rows). If one of the heterozygous normals marries a homozygous normal, all offspring will be phenotypically normal but half of them will be heterozygous. This distribution may continue for a number of generations in which the abnormality will never appear as a visible trait, though it is carried along as a recessive allele in the heterozygotes. If two heterozygous parents now chance to mate, the result will be a simple Mendelian segregation, ¼ of the children being homozygous recessives and abnormal. From this pedigree we can see how, in a family free for generations from a hereditary abnormality, perhaps a type of feeble-mindedness, abnormal children may suddenly appear; by bad luck both parents of the affected child were heterozygous for the proper gene. This situation also explains why consanguineous marriages, such

73

as cousin marriages, may produce abnormal offspring more often than other matings. In itself consanguinity is not harmful. If both parents come from stock lacking harmful genes, the children will have no aberrant features. If it were really true that the Pharaohs of ancient Egypt or the Aztec royalty had genes for

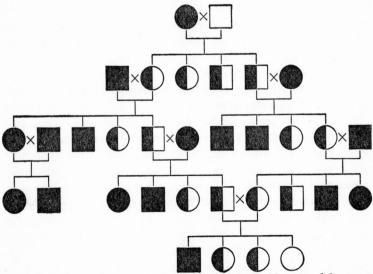

Fig. 23. Pedigree of a recessive human trait. Black is the *normal* dominant phenotype; black-white, the heterozygous individuals. White is the recessive trait, always homozygous if visible. (This is not the usual way of drawing a recessive pedigree, but rather one meant to make the facts at once visible. The usual way is to draw the abnormals black and all normals white, i.e., in this case, all would be marked white except the 2 white persons in the figure, the male at the top and the female at the bottom, the 2 homozygous recessives, who would be marked black.)

strikingly superior qualities, the law of brother-sister marriage in these households would have been genetically wise. But, unfortunately, so many recessive genes for abnormalities and malfunctions are floating about in human populations that few families can be completely free from them. Therefore, the probability that some unwelcome recessive will be present in two cousins is high, certainly much higher than in unrelated individuals, and offspring of the union of cousins are thus more likely to be homozygous recessives. The fourth and fifth generations of

74

Fig. 23 represent this situation in the marriage of second-degree cousins.

The rest of Fig. 23 can be read as follows: In the first row a homozygous normal woman (black) marries an abnormal recessive man (white). All the children are normal and heterozygous (second row). One heterozygous daughter (left) marries a homozygous normal man; their children are again normal, half of them homozygous, half carriers of the recessive allele. One of the homozygous normal daughters marries a normal man (third row, left). Children born to them are all homozygous normal (fourth row, left). In the F_2 family a heterozygous son marries a homozygous normal girl (third row, center); their offspring are normal, although half are heterozygous. One of the heterozygous sons in the F_1 also married a homozygous normal girl (second row, right) and sired normal children, half of whom are heterozygous (third row, right). One of these third-generation heterozygous daughters marries a normal man; once more, in the fourth generation, all children are normal but half are heterozygous (fourth row, right). In this generation second cousins marry. Among their children, the fifth generation, 1 daughter is homozygous recessive and exhibits the abnormality, which had not been seen in the family since the marriage of the great-great-grandparent of this unhappy girl. It should again be stressed that, for a family of only 2 children, in place of the theoretical expectation of $\frac{1}{4}$ abnormals this cousin marriage might in actuality give, by chance, 2 abnormals, or 1, or none.

These two pedigrees were drawn with the genetic constitution indicated for the heterozygotes, so that the pedigree is immediately interpretable. The human geneticist, in drawing up a pedigree for an actual family tree, will at the beginning know only which individuals exhibit the character being studied and which do not. In his chart no black-white symbols would appear. The heterozygotes in the dominance pedigree would be black, as they would in the recessive pedigree. In practice, in the recessive pedigree, one would represent the abnormals as black, the normals as white, to facilitate quick recognition of the former. To avoid confusion, this was not done in our pedigree. A real pedigree would therefore resemble our Fig. 1 for bleeder's disease, this being a recessive with a complication we shall analyze presently.

To conclude this brief section on elementary human heredity a little story can be told which shows that even a court of law may recognize the stringency of Mendel's laws. In Norway an illegitimate child is entitled to the name and estate of the father, and paternity suits there are understandably numerous. In one such case, Hans O. denied being the father of the child of Karen H. When all other arguments had been exhausted, the mother pointed out that her child had fingers with one joint missing (the technical name for this is brachydactyly) and that Hans O. had exactly the same peculiarity. The court thereupon summoned a well-known geneticist. He testified that brachydactyly is a familiar dominant Mendelian trait that has been analyzed in many pedigrees. The identity of the abnormality in the presumptive father and child was proved by an X-ray photograph. The mother and all her relatives had normal fingers, and the abnormality had never been seen in the whole neighborhood, which Hans O. had visited for only a short time. Therefore, the probability that another man with the same rather infrequent abnormality was the father could be considered to be practically nil. The court declared Hans O. the father.

4

More on Elementary Mendelism

Mendelian heredity with more than one pair of alleles

When Mendel carried out his experiments on peas in the monastery garden plot, he studied 7 pairs of alleles, including, as noted previously, those for yellow vs. green seeds, for purple vs. white flowers, as well as alleles for tall vs. short stems, round vs. wrinkled seeds, green vs. yellow unripe pods, and others. Each pair behaved in exactly the same way, with uniform dominance in the F_1, segregation in a 3 : 1 ratio in the F_2, segregation in a 1 : 1 ratio in a backcross. Mendel, however, did not stop here; he went on to ask himself what would be seen if he followed 2 or 3 or more pairs of alleles simultaneously into the F_2. (In fact, being a very clever man, Mendel so designed his experiments from the beginning that he could obtain the answers from the same set of experiments as he used for the simple case of 1 pair of alleles.) Thus he crossed, let us say, purple-flowered yellow-seed plants with white-flowered green-seed plants, or purple, yellow, and tall ones with white, green, and small. The all-important result of such experiments was that each pair of alleles segregated in a Mendelian way quite independently, exactly as though the others were not present. What this means will be clear when we analyze an example in detail. For a change, we shall use guinea pigs as experimental material.

Among the many varieties of guinea pigs bred by fanciers are stocks differing in color—blacks, whites, piebalds, etc.—and others varying in the character of the fur—Angora, rough, etc. For our experiment we select 2 true-breeding, homozygous strains, a short-haired black and a white with long, silky, so-called Angora hair. Previous crosses, we know at the outset, have shown that

77

black and white are dependent on 1 pair of alleles, black being dominant to white; similarly, long and short hair are due to a pair of alleles, with short dominant to long. A cross of the 2 varieties then reads, in the notation used earlier:

$$\frac{\text{Black}}{\text{Black}} \quad \frac{\text{Short}}{\text{Short}} \times \frac{\text{white}}{\text{white}} \quad \frac{\text{long}}{\text{long}}$$

The F_1 is evidently

$$\frac{\text{Black}}{\text{white}} \quad \frac{\text{Short}}{\text{long}}$$

Since Black and Short are dominant (indicated by capitals), the hybrid is phenotypically a short-haired black. Now, we remember, the basic fact upon which Mendelian segregation rests is the purity of the gametes produced by the hybrid. Neglecting the hair character for the moment and dealing only with color, we know that the hybrid will form equal numbers of gametes containing the black gene or its white allele. And, putting aside color to follow hair type, we know that the hybrid will form gametes of which half contain the gene for short hair and half the recessive allele for long hair. What happens when we follow both pairs of alleles simultaneously? Mendel grasped the simple answer to this question in a flash of insight, after he observed the actual F_2 results. He saw—and this is his second great discovery, following upon the law of purity of gametes—that the 2 pairs of alleles are distributed to the gametes completely independently of one another. Two types of sex cells, in equal numbers according to chance, are formed, with black or white, and, simultaneously and also in equal numbers, 2 types with short or long. Since every sex cell must receive 1 member of each pair of alleles, and since each pair is distributed without reference to the other, $2 \times 2 = 4$ kinds of sex cells must be produced. This is exactly what one would have in a game of dice played with 2 dice, one having the number 1 on 3 faces and the number 2 on the other 3 faces, the second marked in the same way with 3 and 4. In a game of many throws the 4 possible combinations, 1 and 3, 1 and 4, 2 and 3, 2 and 4 will come up in nearly equal numbers. Just so in the game of the sex cells: Equal numbers of the 4 types of gametes will appear: Black-Short, Black-long, white-Short, white-long. In the language of genetics, there is

78

an independent assortment of the alleles in the gametes; the hybrid forms equal numbers of as many types of gametes as possible for combinations among the 2 pairs. This is equally true, we may add, for 3 or more pairs of alleles in all simple cases of Mendelian heredity.

In our experiment, then, an F_1 female hybrid producing these 4 kinds of eggs is mated to a brother who has the same 4 types of sperm cells, and their progeny are the second hybrid generation, the F_2. If, as we know is the case, chance alone determines what egg is fertilized by a given sperm, there must be $4 \times 4 = 16$ possible fertilizations, each type occurring as often as every other. A very simple method for visualizing these 16 possible F_2 combinations is to use a so-called Roman square. To construct it, we divide a square into 16 small squares. Above the columns of small squares we write the 4 types of gametes formed by the F_1 hybrid, and along one vertical side of the horizontal rows we again list these gametes. This being our first use of the method, we shall write out the names of the alleles, i.e., the phenotype they control. Next we draw a horizontal line in each square and enter above each line in a vertical column (squares 1, 5, 9, 13, etc.) the type of gamete given at the top: Black-Short in the first column, Black-long in the second, etc. Below the line of each square we fill in for each horizontal row the gamete listed at the left: for squares 1, 2, 3, 4 Black-short; for squares 5, 6, 7, 8, Black-long; etc. Thus we derive all 16 possible F_2 combinations, writing each in the form of a fraction, as we have done heretofore. In practice, the geneticist simplifies the procedure by using symbols in place of the words, as Mendel himself did. He suggested indicating a pair of alleles by the same letter, using a capital for the dominant, a lower-case letter for the recessive. Thus, Black would be abbreviated to B and white to b, Short to S and long to s. The advantage of this method is obvious; it can be seen immediately that BB is a homozygous black, bb a homozygous white, Bb a heterozygous Black, $BbSs$ an individual heterozygous for Black-white and for Short-long and phenotypically short-haired black. For clarity, both the symbols and the interpretive words have been entered in the following Roman square. Hereafter, however, we should be content to use only the letter symbols, which give all the information in the smallest space.

Eggs	Black-Short	Black-long	white-Short	white-long
1. Black-Short	**1** $\dfrac{\text{Black-Short}}{\text{Black-Short}}$ $\dfrac{BS}{BS}$ Both dom. homoz. Pheno: black-short	**2** $\dfrac{\text{Black-long}}{\text{Black-Short}}$ $\dfrac{Bs}{BS}$ B homoz., S heteroz. black-short	**3** $\dfrac{\text{white-Short}}{\text{Black-Short}}$ $\dfrac{bS}{BS}$ S homoz., B heteroz. black-short	**4** $\dfrac{\text{white-long}}{\text{Black-Short}}$ $\dfrac{bs}{BS}$ Both heteroz. black-short
2. Black-long	**5** $\dfrac{\text{Black-Short}}{\text{Black-long}}$ $\dfrac{BS}{Bs}$ B homoz., S heteroz. Pheno: black-short	**6** $\dfrac{\text{Black-long}}{\text{Black-long}}$ $\dfrac{Bs}{Bs}$ B homoz., s homoz. black-long	**7** $\dfrac{\text{white-Short}}{\text{Black-long}}$ $\dfrac{bS}{Bs}$ Both heteroz. black-short	**8** $\dfrac{\text{white-long}}{\text{Black-long}}$ $\dfrac{bs}{Bs}$ B heteroz., s homoz. black-long
3. white-Short	**9** $\dfrac{\text{Black-Short}}{\text{white-Short}}$ $\dfrac{BS}{bS}$ B heteroz., S homoz. Pheno: black-short	**10** $\dfrac{\text{Black-long}}{\text{white-Short}}$ $\dfrac{Bs}{bS}$ Both heteroz. black-short	**11** $\dfrac{\text{white-Short}}{\text{white-Short}}$ $\dfrac{bS}{bS}$ b and S homoz. white-short	**12** $\dfrac{\text{white-long}}{\text{white-Short}}$ $\dfrac{bs}{bS}$ b homoz., S heteroz. white-short
4. white-long	**13** $\dfrac{\text{Black-Short}}{\text{white-long}}$ $\dfrac{BS}{bs}$ Both heteroz. Pheno: black-short	**14** $\dfrac{\text{Black-long}}{\text{white-long}}$ $\dfrac{Bs}{bs}$ B heteroz., s homoz. black-long	**15** $\dfrac{\text{white-Short}}{\text{white-long}}$ $\dfrac{bS}{bs}$ b homoz., S heteroz. white-short	**16** $\dfrac{\text{white-long}}{\text{white-long}}$ $\dfrac{bs}{bs}$ b, s homoz. white-long

What the Roman square teaches

From this square we can read many important facts about the nature of the F_2 generation. We first wish to know the phenotypes of the 16 genotypes. Black and Short being dominant, all combinations containing at least 1 of each dominant will be black and short-haired. Black and short both may be homozygous or heterozygous, and we can expect individuals homozygous for both. Only 1 such guinea pig occurs (among 16), in square 1. We can also find animals homozygous for black but heterozygous for short; 2 such combinations appear in squares 2 and 5. Further, we expect some homozygous for short and heterozygous for black; these are to be found in squares 3 and 9. Finally, both allelic pairs may be heterozygous: squares 4, 7, 10, 13. All told, $\frac{9}{16}$ of the F_2 guinea pigs show both dominant traits; but genetically only 1 is completely homozygous, 2 are homozygous for 1 pair and heterozygous for the other alleles, 2 more have the inverse condition, and 4 are heterozygous for both. All this is indicated in four ways in the Roman square: (1) by fractions, using words to indicate the kind of gamete derived from each parent; (2) by similar fractions but using symbols; (3) according to homozygosity or heterozygosity; (4) by phenotype.

Continuing our study of the Roman square, we see that 3 squares, 6, 8, and 14, have black homozygous or heterozygous with the homozygous recessive long. In 3 others, 11, 12, and 15, short is homozygous or heterozygous and white is homozygous recessive. Thus $\frac{3}{16}$ show 1 dominant trait and 1 recessive; another $\frac{3}{16}$, the opposite. Only 1 square remains, number 16, which is homozygous for both recessives. So we find the classic Mendelian F_2 ratio for 2 pairs of alleles, technically called a *dihybrid* situation: 9 : 3 : 3 : 1. This means that $\frac{9}{16}$ of the individuals have the phenotype of both dominants; $\frac{3}{16}$ each, the phenotype of one (or the other) dominant and one (or the other) recessive; and $\frac{1}{16}$ the pure double recessive phenotype. The experiment is illustrated by Fig. 24.

Let us look at some of the consequences of this segregation. Our original cross was between black short-haired and white long-haired guinea pigs. In the F_1 the phenotype showed only the dominant characters, but in the F_2 the grandparental types reappeared. In addition, however, the 2 possible new combina-

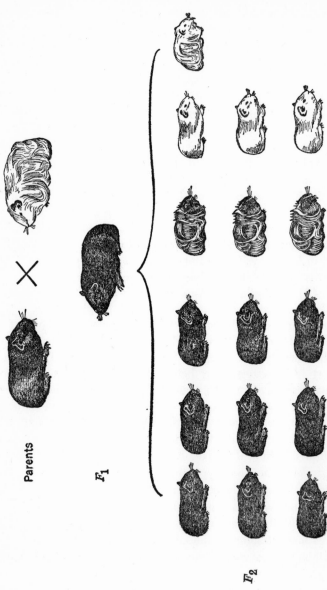

Parents

F_1

F_2

Fig. 24. Parents, F_1, and F_2 of a cross involving 2 pairs of alleles in guinea pigs, black vs. white, short hair vs. long hair, black and short being the dominants.

tions turned up, black-long and white-short. In other words, hybridization resulted in a regrouping that permitted the production of all possible new combinations. Among these novel types, 1 of 3 individuals was homozygous. If this were not a guinea pig but a self-fertilizing plant, we could immediately establish a true-breeding homozygous strain with the new combination of phenotypes. It should be noted that regrouping into all possible new combinations will just as surely occur after hybridization involving 3, 4, and more allelic differences. From this fact it is evident that hybridization followed by *extraction*, as it is called, of F_2 recombinations can be a means for breeding new types from old, available stocks. We shall return to this point presently.

Looking once more at the Roman square, we note that the 4 squares in the diagonal from 1 to 16 (1, 6, 11, 16) contain only homozygous combinations, actually the 4 possible homozygotes: for both dominants (1), for one (or the other) dominant and one (or the other) recessive (6, 11), and for both recessives (16). All other squares represent animals heterozygous for at least 1 pair of alleles. All these heterozygotes will behave like hybrids and, if bred for another generation, will segregate according to their own and their mating partner's constitutions. The only homozygotes we can distinguish phenotypically are the pure recessives (square 16); should we find a pair in our F_2 broods (expected among 32 progeny and certainly found among larger numbers of F_2), we could easily extract this type for further breeding. But suppose that, for some reason, we are anxious to extract a true-breeding line of the new combination long-haired black. Such animals will certainly always be homozygous for the recessive long hair, so that long-haired guinea pigs will breed true. But the dominant black may be homozygous or heterozygous in the $\frac{3}{16}$ of the progeny which are black-long. In pairing black-long animals, it is evidently rather improbable that we shall happen to select 2 homozygotes. We should be much more likely to take 2 heterozygotes or 1 homozygote and 1 heterozygote. If we use 2 heterozygotes, the next generation will segregate again into 3 blacks: 1 white (the recessive long hair is always homozygous and need no longer be considered in this example). Our situation is not improved, for 2 of the 3 new blacks are also

83

heterozygous. Yet all we can do is to select, in each generation, black long-haired guinea pigs (or make many simultaneous matings) in the hope that we shall eventually chance to hit upon a pair of homozygotes and thus establish the desired strain. As was already said, the plant breeder is in a better situation, if his plants permit self-fertilization, for homozygotes will then show up in a single breeding test. It is obvious that in animals in such a case it may happen that in any generation we use a heterozygote with a homozygote. The result—recall the dominant backcross—will simulate the establishment of the desired true-breeding line for the dominant (plus, of course, the homozygous recessive). But after a number of generations of repeated backcrosses of this kind we may be undeceived, for 2 heterozygotes may chance to mate, whereupon the recessive will segregate out. We can readily appreciate how bewildered experimenters must have been in the face of apparently irreconcilable results before Mendel's elegant laws explained hereditary transmission simply, predictably, and demonstrably.

One further point should be appended to this analysis of simple dihybrid segregation. In our example, one of the original parents for the cross was homozygous for both dominants, the other for both recessives, or, in symbols, $BBSS \times bbss$. It would, however, have been possible to make a cross between 2 individuals, each homozygous for a dominant and a recessive: to mate a black, long-haired female to a white, short-haired male (or vice versa); in symbols this would be $BBss \times bbSS$. Eggs of the female would have carried Bs, and sperm of the male bS; the F_1 hybrid would have been $BbSs$, or exactly like the hybrid in the previous cross. The F_2 would therefore be representable by exactly the same Roman square. But in this case the *new* combinations would be the double dominant and the double recessive. Since the phenotype with both homozygous recessives (number 16), $bbss$, directly reflects its genotype, it is easy to select this new recombination in the F_2. In practical breeding this is a frequently used method.

An experiment with 3 pairs of alleles

After the foregoing detailed analysis, it should be easy to derive the results when 3 or more pairs of alleles are involved in a single cross. In the dihybrid case two points were decisive:

The hybrid formed as many types of gametes as there were possible combinations among the 2 pairs of alleles; and fertilization at random gave all these gametes from both parents equal chances to unite. In consequence, the F_1 produced 4 types of gametes and 16 F_2 combinations appeared. In the same way, a trihybrid (3 pairs of alleles) will produce gametes with all possible combinations of the 3 pairs. Using the original simple symbols suggested by Mendel, with capitals for dominants and small letters for recessives, we write the F_1 hybrid as $AaBbCc$, to represent any hereditary traits we please in whatever organism we elect to study. It is readily seen that 8 combinations of these alleles are possible; i.e., equal numbers of 8 types of gametes will be produced by the F_1:

All 3 dominants	**1.** *ABC*
Two dominants, 1 recessive	
recessive *a*	**2.** *aBC*
recessive *b*	**3.** *AbC*
recessive *c*	**4.** *ABc*
One dominant, 2 recessives	
dominant *A*	**5.** *Abc*
dominant *B*	**6.** *aBc*
dominant *C*	**7.** *abC*
All 3 recessives	**8.** *abc*

With these 8 types of gametes, $8 \times 8 = 64$ types of fertilization are possible. With 4 pairs of alleles, 16 types of gametes and 16×16 types of fertilizations are possible. Ten pairs of alleles form 1024 types of gametes and 1024×1024, or more than a million, F_2 combinations. In every case, of course, the combinations appear in definite numerical ratios that can easily be computed.

Certain consequences of these facts are worth noting. Let us suppose that members of 2 human races, differing in 10 pairs of independent alleles (later we shall find that 24 such pairs are possible), are crossed. More than a million grandchildren, the F_2 individuals, would be required to provide a fair probability of including all possible combinations; if each single pair of original parents have 4 grandchildren, we should need (assuming, for simplicity, brother-sister matings) more than a quarter of a million F_2 families to have a minimal opportunity for each possible combination to appear even once in the F_2. In another case, we may have 2 strains of domestic plants or animals differing in 10 pairs of alleles, each line having some of the dominants and some of the recessives. We wish to establish a breed having all the recessives. As we can now understand, only 1 individual homozygous for recessives for all 10 genes is to be expected among more than a million F_2 individuals. Imagine carrying out this experiment with horses or cattle!

	Eggs	BSR	BSr	BsR	bSR	Bsr	bSr	bsR	bsr
Sperm									
	BSR	BSR BSR 1	BSr BSR 2	BsR BSR 3	bSR BSR 4	Bsr BSR 5	bSr BSR 6	bsR BSR 7	bsr BSR 8
	BSr	BSR BSr 9	BSr BSr 10	BsR BSr 11	bSR BSr 12	Bsr BSr 13	bSr BSr 14	bsR BSr 15	bsr BSr 16
	BsR	BSR BsR 17	BSr BsR 18	BsR BsR 19	bSR BsR 20	Bsr BsR 21	bSr BsR 22	bsR BsR 23	bsr BsR 24
	bSR	BSR bSR 25	BSr bSR 26	BsR bSR 27	bSR bSR 28	Bsr bSR 29	bSr bSR 30	bsR bSR 31	bsr bSR 32
	Bsr	BSR Bsr 33	BSr Bsr 34	BsR Bsr 35	bSR Bsr 36	Bsr Bsr 37	bSr Bsr 38	bsR Bsr 39	bsr Bsr 40
	bSr	BSR bSr 41	BSr bSr 42	BsR bSr 43	bSR bSr 44	Bsr bSr 45	bSr bSr 46	bsR bSr 47	bsr bSr 48
	bsR	BSR bsR 49	BSr bsR 50	BsR bsR 51	bSR bsR 52	Bsr bsR 53	bSr bsR 54	bsR bsR 55	bsr bsR 56
	bsr	BSR bsr 57	BSr bsr 58	BsR bsr 59	bSR bsr 60	Bsr bsr 61	bSr bsr 62	bsR bsr 63	bsr bsr 64

Now let us look at the Roman square for 3 pairs of alleles (Roman squares for more than 3 pairs would be rather cumbersome, but it should be clear that everything one can read from such a square can readily be computed with the aid of a few simple arithmetical formulae). We shall use guinea pigs, as in the dihybrid example, merely taking parents with an additional pair of genic differences, namely, rough fur (dominant) vs. smooth fur (recessive). The 3 pairs of alleles are thus:

> BB black vs. bb white
> SS short hair vs. ss long hair
> RR rough fur vs. rr smooth fur

The F_1 hybrid is $BbSsRr$, phenotypically black, short, rough; it produces 8 types of gametes: BSR, BSr, BsR, bSR, Bsr, bSr, bsR, bsr. The 64 F_2 combinations are given in the Roman square, this time represented only by symbols.

It should hardly be necessary to discuss all the results to be seen in the square, for they are in principle the same as those found in the dihybrid cross except, of course, for the numerical relations. Attention may be directed to a few details. Once more the number of homozygous combinations equals the number of F_1 gamete types, 8, and again these combinations are found along the diagonal through squares 1, 10, 19, 28, 37, 46, 55, 64. One is homozygous for all 3 dominants (square 1) and 1 for all 3 recessives (square 64). The remaining 56 combinations are heterozygous for 1, 2, or all 3 allelic pairs, equal numbers of them being heterozygous for B alone, or S, or R, or BS, etc. Counting the number of phenotypes, as before, and keeping in mind the dominance of B, S, and R, we obtain 8 distinct phenotypes, as follows:

27 among 64 with the phenotype of all 3 dominants BSR, i.e., appearing black, short, rough.
   (Nos. 1–9, 11, 12, 15, 17, 18, 20, 22, 25, 26, 27, 29, 33, 36, 41, 43, 49, 50, 57.)
9 among 64 with BS (2 dominants) and r (1 recessive), i.e., appearing black, short, smooth.
   (Nos. 10, 13, 14, 16, 34, 38, 42, 45, 58.)

9 among 64 with *BR* (2 dominants) and *s* (1 recessive), i.e., appearing black, long, rough.

(Nos. 19, 21, 23, 24, 35, 39, 51, 53, 59.)

9 among 64 with *SR* (2 dominants) and *b* (1 recessive), i.e., appearing white, short, rough.

(Nos. 28, 30, 31, 32, 44, 47, 52, 54, 60.)

3 among 64 *B* (1 dominant) and *sr* (2 recessives), i.e., appearing black, long, smooth.

(Nos. 37, 40, 61.)

3 among 64 *S* (1 dominant) *br* (2 recessives), i.e., appearing white, short, smooth.

(Nos. 46, 48, 62.)

3 among 64 *R* (1 dominant) *bs* (2 recessives), i.e., appearing white, long, rough.

(Nos. 55, 56, 63.)

1 among 64 *bsr* (all 3 recessives) (homozygous), i.e., appearing white, long, smooth.

(No. 64.)

Here we have an obviously varied F_2. But now imagine a situation like that seen in the four-o'clocks, where the heterozygotes could be distinguished as intermediate pink-flowered plants. If *Bb* and *Ss* and *Rr* were similarly distinct, we should be able to identify the heterozygotes and their combinations and have an even greater number of F_2 phenotypes, as can be read from the Roman square.

It was previously noted that these expectations can be derived arithmetically. A single example of this procedure may suffice for the present. The phenotypic ratio, assuming dominance of one member of each pair of alleles, can be obtained thus:

No. of Pairs of Alleles	Gametic Assortment	Phenotypic Ratio
1	$(3 + 1)$	$3 : 1$
2	$(3 + 1) \times (3 + 1)$	$9 : 3 : 3 : 1$
3	$(3 + 1) \times (3 + 1) \times (3 + 1)$	$27 : 9 : 9 : 9 : 3 : 3 : 3 : 1$
4	$(3 + 1) \times (3 + 1) \times (3 + 1) \times (3 + 1)$	$81 : 27 : 27 : 27 : 27 :$ $9 : 9 : 9 : 9 : 9 : 9 :$ $3 : 3 : 3 : 3 : 1$

Essentially similar calculations will give the number of types of gametes, of F_2 homozygotes, of F_2 heterozygotes where heterozygotes are distinguishable, etc.

88

Mendelism and breeding

We are now prepared to examine certain general consequences of the elementary rules of Mendelian segregation. In the first chapter we discussed the procedures of the plant improver and animal breeder; it was emphasized there that the old and widely successful method for developing better crop plants and live-stock is selection of the best individuals in each generation for further breeding. We learned that the breeder is successful be-cause what initially seems to be a single, though variable, line or race is actually a mixture of several to many hereditary constitu-tions, which are separated by selection. It was further noted that a better understanding of these facts would be possible for us after study of the laws of inheritance. The information we have acquired up to this point is not, in fact, sufficient for a full understanding of what happens in practical selection work, and we shall need to return to the problem after consideration of certain special features of Mendelism in a later chapter. One aspect of successful breeding is, however, a direct consequence of Mendelian recombination and may therefore be discussed here.

A famous engraving by Albrecht Dürer depicts the prodigal son with his herd of swine. Here the artist has preserved for us the external form, the phenotype, if you will, of the domestic pig of fifteenth- and sixteenth-century Europe, an animal not far removed from the wild boar. Compare it with the modern porker: The twentieth-century provider of lard and ham is more than twice the size of his ancestor, many times as heavy, padded with a thick coat of fat, and so formed that its belly almost sweeps the ground, while the legs and snout are short. The contrasts reflect the efforts of breeders over the past four or five centuries. Could they have accomplished so much simply by breeding from, say, the fattest individuals in each generation? As we shall see, only limited success would have come from so doing. Today's prize hog would not exist had not British breed-ers imported from Eastern Asia a strain of pigs with an inherited tendency to accumulate great masses of fat and hybridized this strain with their domestic pig. Later on, still other foreign lines were crossed with the partly improved native breeds. Eventu-ally, out of the rich store of genetic diversity thus brought to-

89

gether, Mendelian recombinations appeared which, when selected and made homozygous, sired the modern breed. The breeders thus carried out a complicated Mendelian experiment, although they approached the problem empirically. Had they been aware of the laws discovered by Mendel, their task could have been completed more rapidly and efficiently; contemporary breeders go about their projects in essentially the same way, hybridization and selection of recombinations.

Another example can be taken from plant breeding. In Sweden, extending from moderate temperate to arctic latitudes, it is of obvious economic importance to move the wheat-growing region as far north as possible. The good wheats grown in the south of Sweden originally could not endure the frigid winters and short summers of the north. Strains of wheat were known which are genetically adapted to survival in the more rigorous climates, but they are poor in yield, nutritive and milling qualities, etc. The problem confronting Swedish geneticists was to combine, by crossing and extraction of segregating recombinants, the desired qualities of southern wheats with the cold hardiness of the poorer wheats. So successful were they in putting together the needed combination that the wheat-growing region was pushed much farther north and great additions accrued to the national granary.

A different but highly important aspect of the same practical problem arises from the need for resistance in crop plants to disease, such as smuts and blights. Wheat, for example, suffers from a smut that causes millions of dollars' damage each year. Geneticists found some otherwise poor strains of wheat which carried a hereditary factor making them smut-resistant. Accordingly, an experiment was inaugurated to insert this capacity for resistance to smut into a plant having the other good qualities of the susceptible varieties, using the method of hybridization and extraction of Mendelian recombinants. The successful result has been of enormous benefit to producers and consumers alike.

Another example can be taken from everyday life. A new "race" of dogs may appear on the market and sweep the field, as did the Doberman pinscher not very many years ago. How did this novelty originate? The breeder will certainly not divulge what he did. But we can now take it for granted that in most cases—other possibilities will be considered later on—he crossed existing races, generally in a haphazard way, looked for combinations in the segregating generations which struck him as good, crossed and selected again and perhaps again. When he had finally combined the nose of one race, the leg length of another, the color, hair texture and length, head shape, tail form, body size, etc., from still others into a promising mixture, he made the combination as homozygous as possible by inbreeding and discarding the non-conformists, until the new type was sufficiently pure-breeding or homozygous to be marketed. Usually, in such cases, segregation continues for characters that, for genetic reasons, cannot be homozygous; in practice this genetic situation is taken care of by killing off the "runts" and "culls."

Our knowledge of elementary Mendelism also permits us to view in proper perspective the claims of the so-called "plant wizards" who, in various countries, have claimed to have achieved success, itself incontestable and valuable, in the production of new varieties by all sorts of mystical procedures and techniques. As we can clearly understand, what they actually did was to collect from all over the world strains and lines of the plant to be improved and to choose—and here the practical genius of these men came into play—those with the most promising characteristics. These were hybridized and the hybrids again crossed to other types, the crosses being based not on a scientifically guided plan but on a hit-or-miss method, so that their results could not later be unraveled. Eventually, in innumerable trials, chance supplied the Mendelian recombinations sought. In many plants these could be used immediately, without being made homozygous, since they could be propagated by cuttings. The wizard had been no more—if no less—than an unwitting but clever Mendelian; the sorcery was the Mendelian processes of inheritance.

Man again

This chapter may end with a note on man. It has already been stressed that all inherited traits in which people differ depend upon Mendelizing genes, including factors whose heredity is of the more complex types that we shall study later. Among human inherited traits we can list: skull shape, as long

91

vs. round; form of forehead, nose, jaw; arrangement of teeth; overall body size; form and number of specific bones, as length of femur and number of digits; details of arrangement or structure of specific muscles, as the calf muscles and facial muscles; form of the eyelids; type of hair, whether straight, curly, or kinky; color of hair, eyes, and skin; longevity; tendency to bear twins; details of blood chemistry; metabolic variations; secretory differences; body build, as stockiness and slenderness; shape of eyeball, as involved in near-sightedness; sensory discriminatoriness, as ability to taste and smell a given substance; the majority of non-infectious eye, skin, and ear abnormalities of function; a large number of other abnormalities or diseases of all organs; numerous mental and nervous qualities, within and beyond the range of so-called normality; and specific talents, as for music and mathematics. (In all cases, of course, alleles are paired alternatives: allele for normal vs. allele for long life span; allele for clubfoot vs. allele for normal foot; etc.)

From this fragmentary list we can be sure, especially in view of the former discussion of the work of plant and animal breeders, that any Martian superbeings who may come to Earth and begin breeding men for pets or for perfect efficiency would use exactly the same methods, conscious or unconscious, as the livestock improver. As visualized in a widely read satire, the Martian could obtain, from such Mendelian recombinations, stupid muscle machines for heavy labor, long-lived brain-men as inventors, fat and succulent porkers for meat, and dwarfs with split noses, bowlegs, and similar attractive features as pets for the conquerors' ladies.

5

Chromosomes
and Mendelism

Introduction and statement of basic facts

We have now learned that the essential facts, the elementary rules, of Mendelian inheritance are the following: (1) The gametes formed by a hybrid are pure for one or the other allele of each pair of factors present in the hybrid itself and derived from its parents. (2) In the sex cells of the hybrid all possible combinations of alleles of all the different pairs occur, each gamete containing one partner of every pair. (3) Equal numbers of the several genetic kinds of gametes occur. (4) Fertilization takes place according to chance, so that each kind of gamete formed by the F_1 female may be fertilized by any of the kinds of male gametes. It is obvious that further understanding of the meaning of these facts is to be sought in the sex cells. In them must reside mechanisms ensuring the purity of gametes, the random assortment of alleles in formation of gametes by a hybrid, and the chance result of fertilization. Chapter 2 has, in fact, already taught us what we must know about the cell if we are to interpret the facts of heredity.

Let it be remembered that Mendel knew nothing of cell division, the processes of fertilization, the chromosomes, or reduction division. But by the time Mendel's laws were rediscovered in 1900 all these facts of cell biology had been explored and their probable significance for heredity had already been widely discussed; some relations had, indeed, been correctly forecast. It was therefore not difficult to relate the facts of Mendelism to the nature and behavior of sex cells. Ever since this early union,

93

Mendelism and cytology (the study of cells) have collaborated intimately; from this union has arisen a virile hybrid, cytogenetics, the study of the cellular basis of heredity. The essence of this science can be stated in a single sentence: Each pair of Mendelian alleles is located at definite twin points on a pair of homologous chromosomes; whatever normal or abnormal distribution of the chromosomes takes place will be predictably reflected in the distribution of inheritable characters in the offspring; whatever happens to the chromosomes will become manifest in exactly parallel events related to inheritable characters.

Here may be recapitulated previously discussed facts of cytology which we shall now use: (1) The number of chromosomes in the cells of a given organism is typical, constant, and (generally) even. (2) In ordinary cell division each chromosome is duplicated by formation of an identical daughter chromosome (or seems to split lengthwise). (3) Egg and sperm bring to fertilization the same number and kinds of chromosomes, each having 1 complete set, or half the number typical for body cells. (4) In consequence, in the zygote and in all cells derived from it, with the sole exception of mature gametes, each type of chromosome is represented twice, as a pair of homologues, 1 of maternal and 1 of paternal origin. (5) To make this possible there occur, in the formation of sex cells, the reduction divisions in which the chromosome number is reduced to 1 of each type. One might immediately guess that these maturation divisions have something to do with Mendelism.

Chromosomes and genes in the basic Mendelian cross

We return now to our first Mendelian experiment, the four-o'clock with red or white flowers. Assume that the genes or alleles controlling the production of flower pigments are located at identical points on the 2 members of a pair of homologous chromosomes. To avoid probing into the very difficult and still controversial problem of the actual nature of such a gene, we may, taking the simplest possibility, consider it to be a minute section of a chromosome, different from the rest of the element. In one plant this segment or gene may be the kind conditioning production of red color in petals; in another variety it may be somewhat different, there determining the development of white flowers. The normal chromosome number in this plant is 16, or

8 pairs. For our diagrams, since 16 chromosomes would rather crowd a small figure, we shall eliminate some and assume the number to be 8, or 4 pairs. To make identifiable the chromo-

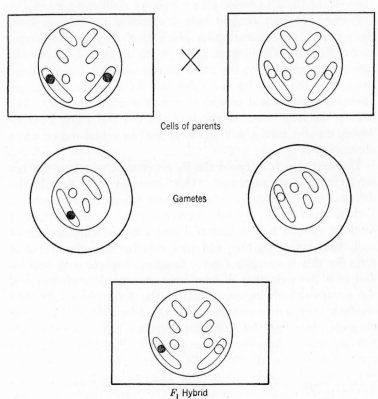

Cells of parents

Gametes

F_1 Hybrid

FIG. 25. The chromosomes of a cross between two plants differing in 1 pair of alleles (black dot vs. white dot). Four pairs of chromosomes are assumed, one of which, the longest, is supposed to contain the alleles, which alone are different in the 2 races. First row the normal chromosome sets; second row the gametes of each form with the reduced number of chromosomes; third row chromosomes of the F_1 hybrid.

some in which we are interested, that containing the gene for flower color, the 4 pairs of chromosomes will be depicted as differing in size. The chromosome with the color gene—it is the largest one in the illustrations—is present as a pair in each cell, 1 partner coming from the mother (seed parent) and 1 from the father (pollen parent). In the pure red-flowered variety both chromosomes carry the gene for red; in the pure white strain both have the gene for white (Fig. 25, first row: black dot = gene for red; white dot = gene for white). These are the cells of the 2 varieties with which we shall experiment.

Mature sex cells contain only 1 chromosome of each kind, their chromosome constitution being that seen in the second row of Fig. 25. Fertilization gives rise to the hybrid; all its cells contain, in addition to the other chromosomes, 1 long chromosome with the gene for red color and its homologue with the allele for development of white color (Fig. 25, third row). For brevity we may hereafter speak of the red and white chromosomes; no one, surely, will expect to find an actual red or white chromosome!

The next step is to breed the F_2 generation, watching the behavior of the chromosomes. Our attention must initially be directed to processes by which mature gametes are formed in both sexes of the F_1 hybrid. Remember the earlier description of these events: how a maternal and paternal chromosome of each kind come together and pair side by side—the technical term for this is *synapsis* (*syn* = together, *haptein* = to stick)— and how the reduction division separates whole chromosomes, the synapsed homologues. Each of the 2 daughter cells thus receives 1 of the homologues. In the four-o'clock hybrid the synapsis preceding the reduction divisions brings together the red and white chromosomes, as shown in Fig. 26A. The succeeding reduction division pulls the red chromosome to one pole, the white to the other (Fig. 26B). This happens in the formation of all the sex cells, with the result that half of the gametes carry the white chromosome, the other half having the red (Fig. 26C, D). Think back, now, to the Mendelian law of purity of gametes and production of the different gamete types in the same number. Clearly, the mechanism underlying this law is the fact—which the cytologist can show one with his microscope, using suitable material—that the mature gametes can contain only the red *or* the white chromosome, not both (meaning, of course, the genes or sections which have been called the red and white alleles). The equivalence of numbers of the 2 types of gametes is simply the outcome of their origin by division of 1 cell into 2 (for reasons already explained, consideration of a second maturation division is omitted).

96

A further Mendelian principle, the segregation in the F_2 of the pure, homozygous parental types and the heterozygotes in the ratio 1 red : 2 pink : 1 white is clearly a simple consequence of the results of the reduction division and the random nature of fertilization. Since chance alone decides which gametes meet at fertilization, an egg with a red chromosome is equally likely to be fertilized by a pollen grain with a red chromosome or one

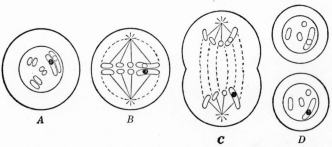

Fig. 26. Maturation divisions of the hybrid in the third row of Fig. 25. (A) Conjugation of homologous chromosomes, (B) equatorial plate of the reduction division, (C) separation of the 2 chromosome sets, (D) the 2 types of gametes containing either the black or the white allele.

with a white chromosome, as indicated by arrows in Fig. 27, upper row; fertilization of an egg with a white chromosome by pollen with a white or pollen with a red chromosome will occur with just the same frequency as shown in Fig. 27, lower row, A–D. Thus we obtain equal numbers of the 4 possible kinds of fertilizations, which then give rise to individuals having the chromosome constitutions red-red, red-white, white-red, white-white. This is the typical Mendelian segregation, and it is fully explained by the fact that a pair of alleles is located at specific, identical points on a pair of homologous chromosomes.

We can now appreciate the simplicity and usefulness of Mendel's original notation, in which he labeled the pairs of alleles Aa, Bb, etc. In Figs. 25–27 we could have used the letter A in place of the black dot on the red chromosome and the letter a on the white chromosome. In Mendelian symbols the parents would then be AA and aa, the F_1 hybrid Aa, and the F_2 segregants $AA + Aa + aA + aa$. Realization of this fact will help the novice to understand why Mendelian symbolism requires 2 letters for each individual, for each letter represents a gene within 1 member of a pair of homologous chromosomes. It should also now be clear why the genetic constitution of an individual was previously written as a fraction—for example, $\frac{\text{Black}}{\text{white}}$ or $\frac{\text{Black}}{\text{white}} \frac{\text{Short}}{\text{long}}$; the line in the fraction represents the line of separation between the 2 homologous chromosomes, the

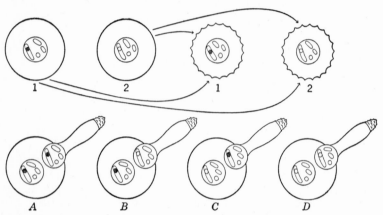

Fig. 27. (*Upper row left*) The 2 types of egg cells, (*right*) the 2 types of pollen. The connecting lines indicate the 4 possible types of union of 2 kinds of eggs with the 2 kinds of sperm. (*Lower row*) The 4 types of fertilization in progress.

space above the line being one chromosome, that below standing for the other.

Chromosomes and genes in Mendelian crosses with more than one pair of alleles

The next important point in Mendel's laws is the free assortment of Mendelizing genes in the gametes of a hybrid containing more than a single pair of independent alleles, as in di-(2), tri-(3), and tetra-(4) hybrids. We have seen that the dihybrid *AaBb* will produce equal numbers of 4 types of gametes, *AB*, *Ab*, *aB*, *ab*, by random recombination of the 2 pairs of alleles *Aa* and *Bb*. We must now see how this fact is the consequence of the location of alleles on homologous chromosomes and of chromosome behavior in reduction divisions. Earlier we studied the pertinent cytological facts (p. 46); all we need now do is to apply them

98

to a specific genetic situation. Once again we may use the example of a cross between a black, short-haired guinea pig and a white, long-haired animal; the actual chromosome number in the guinea pig is 64, but we shall, for simplicity, assume it to be 4 pairs of distinguishable chromosomes. The reader has probably anticipated the conclusion: The pairs of independently segregating alleles are located on different pairs of chromosomes. (Emphasis on "independently segregating" hints at the existence of something outside the pattern of the simple cases of heredity

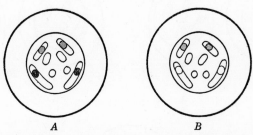

A B

Fig. 28. (A, B) Cells of 2 "races" of an animal differing by 2 pairs of alleles located in 2 pairs of chromosomes (the largest and next largest pair). One pair of alleles (large chromosomes) marked by black and white dots, respectively; the other pair, by parallel-lined vs. stippled dots.

we have thus far examined; this we shall investigate presently.) We can put the pair of black-white alleles in the longest pair of chromosomes, and the allele pair short-long in the next longest chromosome pair (Fig. 28). The chromosomal sections or genes controlling development of black or white we mark with a black or white dot; the genes for hair length, with parallel lines for short and stippling for long. Figure 28A and B represents the cells of the two parent strains, black-short and white-long, with their proper chromosome complements, the 2 sets of homologues. Gametes produced by these parents are pictured in the first row of Fig. 29; below the egg and sperm are cells of the hybrid produced by the mating $A \times B$. It is heterozygous for both pairs of alleles and contains 1 "black" chromosome and 1 "white," plus 1 "short" and 1 "long," in addition to 2 other pairs with which we are not currently concerned.

Again we can expect that the decisive events in the history of the chromosomes, which will explain the free assortment of the pairs of alleles in the gametes, will take place during the reduction division. Reduction begins with pairing or synapsis of all pairs of homologous chromosomes, as Fig. 30, first row, shows. As always happens, the 4 pairs arrange themselves at the cell equator, and then each chromosome separates from its partner, the chromosomes moving as reduced sets into the daughter nu-

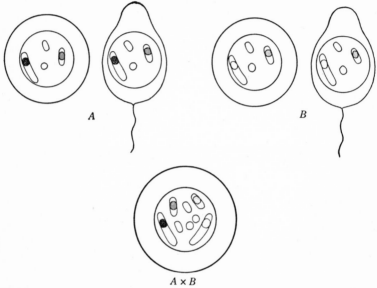

A   *B*

A × B

FIG. 29. (*A*, *B*) Eggs and sperm of the two parents from Fig. 28. (*A* × *B*) The chromosomes of the hybrids between them.

clei of the division figure. Assume that the short-long pair is oriented on the division spindle so that short goes to the north pole and long to the south (Fig. 30, second row). The pair black-white, if its activities are completely independent of the other chromosomes, may be turned so that black faces the south pole (second row, left), or white may be turned southward (Fig. 30, second row, right). The opposite, of course, could also happen, black going north in both cases, but with short facing south in one case, north in the other. Since the result of this orientation is, after the completion of division, precisely the same as for the first arrangement, only the first is diagrammed. The reduction division in these 2 types of cells, differing in regard to

100

the position of the pairs of chromosomes, produces the 4 types of gametes shown in Fig. 30. They contain these combinations of marked chromosomes: (1) black-long, (2) black-short, (3)

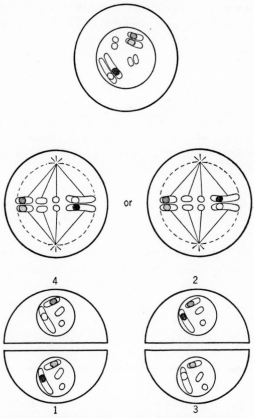

FIG. 30. Reduction divisions in the sex cells of the hybrid. (*First row*) Conjugation (synapsis) of homologous chromosomes. (*Second row*) The 2 possibilities of arrangement in the equatorial plate, i.e., white up, black down vs. black up, white down). (*Third row*) 1–4, the 4 types of sex cells: black-stippled, black-parallel-lined, white-stippled, and white-parallel-lined.

white-long, (4) white-short. These are exactly the 4 types of gametes we expect from a Mendelian dihybrid. We see that the random assortment of independently Mendelizing alleles in the gametes of multiple hybrids is the result of the independence of the chromosomes in taking up their positions on the spindle of

101

the reduction division, this determining to which cell pole each chromosome moves. We still have to account for the fact that the 4 types of gametes are formed in equal numbers. This equality, obviously, requires that the orientation of the pairs of homologous chromosomes during reduction division (in the diagram, north-south vs. south-north) is determined by chance alone and therefore must happen as often one way as the other. Again chromosomal behavior accounts fully for the breeding results from a dihybrid and, needless to say, from trihybrids, tetrahybrids, etc.

Let us interrupt this chromosomal analysis of dihybridism to recall a previous statement that we can now document. It was pointed out that not only all simple inheritance but also all complicated and irregular cases of heredity can be reduced to activities of chromosomes. When the chromosomes behave in the typical fashion just described, the results of crosses follow the Mendelian laws. But where the chromosomes do unexpected things, for whatever reasons, perhaps because of experimental treatment, the breeding results will differ from normal, though they will still be exactly predictable provided that the unusual chromosome events are known. Contrariwise, when things out-of-the-ordinary crop up in inheritance, the geneticist can conclude that something strange must have happened to the chromosomes. One of the great triumphs of the science of genetics has been the correct prediction of results in both directions—namely, from genetical results upon chromosomal behavior, and vice versa—on many occasions. A simple example can be derived from the elementary case we have just analyzed. Suppose that for some reason, known or otherwise, the 2 pairs of chromosomes in the dihybrid (Fig. 30) are prevented from entering the division figure randomly, in regard to their positions, and are forced into orientations which direct all chromosomes from one parent toward the same pole, so that, for example, black and short must go north whereas white and long always go south. Only 2 types of gametes will then be formed; in the F_2 it will seem that black-short and white-long are the effects of only a single pair of genes. If this abnormal result should appear in a cross, examination of the chromosomes would disclose a parallel aberration, perhaps a sticking together of the short and black chromosomes.

It is not difficult to visualize all sorts of disruptions of the beautifully precise normal chromosomal mechanism which would lead to inevitable oddities in the outcome of breeding experiments.

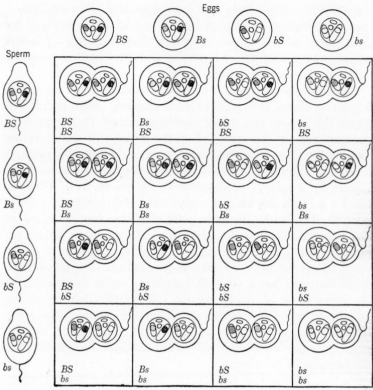

FIG. 31. The 16 types of fertilization possible with the 4 types of eggs and sperm of Fig. 30 presented in the form of the Roman square; (*on top*) the 4 types of eggs and (*left*) the 4 types of sperm. The Mendelian symbols for the 16 combinations are added: *B* stands for black = black dot; *b*, for the recessive allele white = white dot; *S*, for the dominant short hair = parallel-lined dot; *s*, for the recessive long hair = stippled dot.

After this digression we can go back to complete the chromosomal analysis of dihybridism. The 4 types of egg cells and sperm cells (Fig. 30) unite at random in fertilization; as long as chance alone governs which sperm meets a given egg, 16 types of fertilizations will occur in equal numbers. These 16 fertilizations can be represented in a Roman square (Fig. 31), which

103

now shows an egg fusing with a sperm, the chromosomes of each being properly marked. In the same square the Mendelian results are given in the same symbols as were used earlier (*B, b* for black, white; *S, s* for short, long). The complete identity of genetic and cellular facts is at once apparent. Evident, too, is the simplification introduced by the use of letter symbols for description, *as long as we remember that each pair of letters represents a pair of alleles located at definite, identical points on a pair of homologous chromosomes.*

There is no need for us to continue this analysis for more than 2 pairs of alleles in 2 pairs of chromosomes. With pencil and paper the reader can easily convince himself that 3 pairs of chromosomes can be arranged on the equator of the reduction division figure in 4 different ways, so that division will produce 8 types of gametes. Actually this was illustrated previously in Fig. 16 for 4 pairs of chromosomes (see pp. 46, 47). How far can we go with this kind of analysis of polyhybridism (*polys =* many)? Obviously, no more pairs of alleles can be traced in this way than the number of pairs of chromosomes. Man, for example, has 48 chromosomes, or 24 pairs; only 24 pairs of alleles could follow the rules we have so far studied. But no one can think that man has a mere 24 hereditary units; the number of his genes must be vastly greater. A complication enters the picture, to which we devote the following chapter, where the chromosomes, the carriers of the Mendelizing genes, will be even more prominent and will afford dramatic insight into the mechanisms of heredity.

Linkage

At the end of the last chapter we noted that, if Mendelian segregation is based upon the location of the pairs of alleles within chromosomes and upon assortment of the chromosomes in the reduction division and if, further, independently Mendelizing genes are located in different chromosome pairs, it follows that there can be no more independently segregating pairs of alleles in an organism than its number of chromosome pairs. But this certainly cannot mean that the organism has no more genes than half its normal number of chromosomes. Hundreds of allele pairs are known in man, though he has but 24 chromosome pairs; in the little fruit fly so much favored by geneticists almost 1000 have been found, though it has only 4 pairs of chromosomes. In all adequately studied plants and animals—guinea pigs, rabbits, rats, mice, chickens, certain wasps, corn, sweet peas, snapdragons, certain molds—many more pairs of alleles have been described than there are chromosome pairs. The conclusion is inevitable that each chromosome contains numbers of genes.

Many genes in one chromosome

What does this mean for Mendelian heredity? A very rough analogy can be drawn between vehicles and chromosomes carrying genes. All the genes in any one chromosome must travel with the chromosome wherever it goes. The significant movements of these vehicles are those seen in the maturation divisions, which are responsible for Mendelian segregation. All these genes must thus remain together—as long as there is no possibility of their leaving the vehicle—and arrive together in the gametes and fertilized egg. In other words, these genes will

105

Mendelize, segregating as a unit, just as though there were only a single pair of alleles with many different effects. Therefore, a single 3 : 1 ratio in F_2 for all of them together appears. In technical terms, all the genes within a single chromosome would be completely *linked,* inherited as a single package.

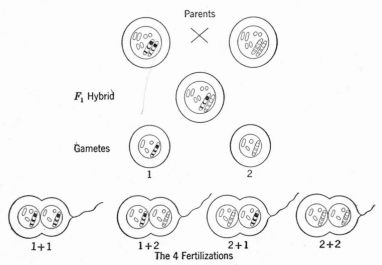

Fig. 32. Behavior of linked genes within a single pair of chromosomes after crossing 2 forms differing in linked pairs of alleles. Three pairs of alleles linked in the same pair of chromosomes are assumed: normal wings vs. curved wings, marked by black vs. white bar; normal legs vs. bow legs, marked by black *V* and white *V*, respectively; and red eyes vs. purple eyes, marked by black vs. white dot. The first row shows cells of parents; the second row, the hybrid cell. The third row represents the gametes of the hybrid; and the last row, the 4 possible fertilizations. (Chromosomes are drawn diagrammatically as in Fig. 31, not as they look in Drosophila.)

Let us take an example from the genetics of the fruit fly, *Drosophila melanogaster,* which we shall use as a test organism in much of this chapter. Among its many known alleles are the following pairs: (1) Normally stretched wings vs. curved wings; normal is dominant over curved, and segregation in the F_2 of a cross gives 3 normal : 1 curved. (2) Normal legs vs. bowlegs; normal is again dominant; in the F_2, 3 normal : 1 bowlegged appear. (3) Normal red eyes vs. purple eyes; red is dominant, and the F_2 segregates into 3 red : 1 purple. These 3 factors can occur separately, each Mendelizing, as we have seen, in the usual way. But we can also find flies having all 3 aberrant traits: curved wings, bowlegs, purple eyes. We may cross such a fly with a normal one, having normal wings, legs, and eyes—called, because flies in nature usually show these normal traits, the *wild type*. The F_1 is the wild type, for all the normal characters are dominant. If the 3 pairs of characters are based upon 3 pairs of alleles located on different chromosomes, we expect (as derived above) in the F_2 the segregation of 8 types in the ratio $27 : 9 : 9 : 9 : 3 : 3 : 3 : 1$. What we actually obtain, upon breeding the F_2, is almost (this "almost" will be explained soon) an ordinary 3 : 1 ratio for wild vs. curved-bow-purple. In other words, the 3 pairs of alleles are linked, they remain together. Despite this fact, their separate existence proves conclusively that they are 3 different allelic pairs and not merely different expressions of a single gene. We conclude that the 3 pairs of alleles are located in the same pair of chromosomes. What happens is shown in Fig. 32, different marks being used for the genes, as explained in the legend. The first row shows the parental cells; the second, the hybrid cells; the third, the gametes of the hybrid; and the fourth, the 4 possible combinations in fertilization.

Tests for linkage groups in different chromosomes

The linkage of all genes located in the same chromosome leads to an interesting problem. Suppose that we know hundreds of pairs of alleles in some organism, each segregating in conventional Mendelian fashion when tested in a breeding experiment. Now take an individual having a character, whatever this may be, based upon a homozygous gene AA; cross it with a specimen having the known gene B, also homozygous or BB. A and B are not alleles (the allele of A would be a; that of B would be b) but are different genes, though we do not yet know whether they are located in the same or different chromosomes. This question we can answer when we have the progeny of such a cross and the F_2 arising from it.

Test made with dominant genes

At this point the beginner in genetics may find himself in trouble. What *is* the F_1 of the cross of the two homozygous dominants $AA \times BB$? In terms of chromosomes, A is a section of a chromosome and B is another section; these segments we call the genes A and B. The AA individual does not exhibit the character B, so it does not have the dominant allele B. Nevertheless, the section of a chromosome which is the gene B in the BB individual must also be present in the AA individual as a chromosomal section which, however, is not B. This means that under the microscope we see in both cases the same sections. But in the BB individual the section, the gene, is chemically (or otherwise) so changed that it produces the effect described as B (say, rough hair), whereas in the AA individual it is not changed (normal hair), is not B. Normal hair if contrasted with rough hair (B) is its recessive condition. Hence, the section that is B in the rough-haired animal's chromosome must be represented in the smooth-haired black guinea pig by the recessive allele of B. In the description we merely omitted reference to the smooth hair of the black animal, for smooth is the usual condition. For a complete description one should have written black, not rough (i.e., smooth), and rough, not black (i.e., wild-type color). The cross was not $AA \times BB$ but $AAbb \times aaBB$, each parent having recessives corresponding to the dominants of the other. It is of the greatest importance that the reader understands clearly these statements. This entire chapter requires attentive reading, though the facts are rather simple.

Now we are ready to continue the analysis of the positional relations of a large number of known pairs of alleles. We cross a fruit fly containing AA, i.e., a dominant gene different from the wild type, with one containing BB, i.e., another, different dominant: in Mendelian symbols, $AAbb \times aaBB$. Two possibilities are evident: (1) A and B are located in 2 different pairs of chromosomes; if so, segregation for the F_2 will yield the ratio typical for 2 independent pairs of alleles, $9 : 3 : 3 : 1$; or (2) A and B are located in the same pair of chromosomes; they are linked. In this case the cross is $\frac{Ab}{Ab} \times \frac{aB}{aB}$. F_1 therefore is $\frac{Ab}{aB}$, and in F_2 segregate $1\frac{Ab}{Ab} : 2\frac{Ab}{aB} : 1\frac{aB}{aB}$, i.e., $\frac{1}{4}$ of the 2 parental forms and $\frac{2}{4}$ with both dominants. (We remember that in this way of writing the line separates the 2 homologous chromosomes, 1 above 1 below the line.) Thus the F_2 result of

¼ each of the parental forms and ⅔ with both dominants proves the location of the 2 dominants in the same chromosome.

Since we are working with fruit flies, we know that 4 pairs of chromosomes are available. Proceeding with the experiment, we determine the results of all possible crosses between 2 different genetic types. If we have at our disposal the types AA, BB, CC, DD, etc. (meaning different distinguishable dominant traits like Lobed eyes, Curly wings, Bar eyes, short Bristles, Eyeless head, etc.), we make the crosses $AA \times BB$, $AA \times CC$, $AA \times DD$, $BB \times CC$, $BB \times DD$, $CC \times DD$, etc. Whenever we obtain in the F_2 a segregation into the phenotypes (A and B now describing the phenotype, not the gene) $9AB : 3A : 3B : 1ab$, we can be confident that A and B are located in different chromosomes. And whenever the F_2 phenotypic ratio is (nearly) $1A : 2AB : 1B$, we can conclude that the 2 genes A and B (or B and C, etc.) are located in the same pair of chromosomes. We can continue to test hundreds of known genes. The cumulative result will be like this:

1. Testing $A \times B$ F_2 ratio $1 : 2 : 1$ A, B in same chromosome
2. Testing $A \times C$ F_2 ratio $9 : 3 : 3 : 1$ A, C in different chromosomes
3. Testing $A \times D$ F_2 ratio $9 : 3 : 3 : 1$ A, D in different chromosomes
4. Testing $C \times D$ F_2 ratio $9 : 3 : 3 : 1$ C, D in different chromosomes
5. Testing $A \times E$ F_2 ratio $9 : 3 : 3 : 1$ A, E in different chromosomes
6. Testing $C \times E$ F_2 ratio $1 : 2 : 1$ C, E in same chromosome
7. Testing $A \times F$ F_2 ratio $9 : 3 : 3 : 1$ A, F in different chromosomes
8. Testing $D \times F$ F_2 ratio $1 : 2 : 1$ D, F in same chromosome
9. Testing $A \times G$ F_2 ratio $9 : 3 : 3 : 1$ A, G in different chromosomes
10. Testing $C \times G$ F_2 ratio $9 : 3 : 3 : 1$ C, G in different chromosomes
11. Testing $D \times G$ F_2 ratio $9 : 3 : 3 : 1$ D, G in different chromosomes
etc.

Test made with recessive genes

Before we continue this analysis it should be emphasized that the result would not be different in principle if the characters with which we were dealing were recessives. In the example mentioned a short time ago, namely, wing, leg, and eye characters of the fruit fly (Fig. 32), the types different from normal or wild type, namely, curved wing, bowleg, and purple eye, were recessives, the normal condition being dominant in each case. Let us assume that we have some such recessive traits, aa, bb, cc $\cdots$, and that it is unknown whether they are

109

located in one or in different chromosomes. Thus we cross aa with bb and breed an F_2. We remember that a recessive gene must be homozygous to produce the visible effect. The one form which shows a but not b is therefore homozygous for a but not for b, and, similarly, the other one is homozygous for b but not for a. Not homozygous for b may mean heterozygous for b (Bb) or homozygous for the normal dominant BB. Let us assume, for simplicity's sake, that the form aa is a homozygous BB, i.e., normal for B, and let us assume the same condition for the form bb, i.e., that it is homozygous AA. Thus our two forms, visibly aa and bb, are really genetically $aaBB$ and $AAbb$. If A and B are located in the same chromosome, this chromosome contains aB in one and Ab in the other form, the hybrid is $\frac{aB}{Ab}$, and in F_2 we shall find the segregation into $1\frac{aB}{aB}$, $1\frac{Ab}{Ab}$, and $2\frac{aB}{Ab}$. The first two are the parental phenotypes aa and bb; the last ones are normals, as both dominants A and B are present. The segregation is therefore into the phenotypes—1 a, 2 normals, and 1 b. If, however, a and b are located in different chromosomes, the F_1 cross is $\frac{aB}{aB} \times \frac{Ab}{Ab}$, the F_1 flies are $\frac{aB}{Ab}$, and the F_2 segregates in the typical dihybrid way into 9 phenotypes with AB (i.e., normals), 3 phenotypes with aa homozygous (i.e., showing the a character), 3 with bb homozygous showing the b character, and 1 $aabb$ showing both recessives. Thus the alternative, same or different chromosome is decided in the case of a recessive trait just as in the dominant case by the segregations 1 : 2 : 1 or 9 : 3 : 3 : 1.

Interpretation

How are these data to be interpreted? Cross 1 in the tabulation on p. 109 proves that A and B are in the same chromosome pair, which we may arbitrarily label chromosome I, defined as the pair containing genes A and B. Cross 2 shows that C is not in chromosome I but in another, which we may call chromosome II. According to No. 6, the gene E is located on this same chromosome. Cross 3 proves that gene D is not on the same chromosome as A, the first chromosome; nor is D on chromosome II (cross 4); we assign it to chromosome III. The gene F, when tested (cross 7), is found not to be linked to *A*, though it is linked with *D* (cross 8). In cross 9 we find gene *G* to be independent of *A*; No. 10 shows that *G* is not linked to *C*; and a third cross (No. 11) excludes it from the chromosome containing *D*. Thus *G*, since it is not on chromosome I or II or III, must be placed on a chromosome IV. We arrive, at length, at this arrangement:

Chromosome	I	II	III	IV
	A	*C*	*D*	*G*
	B	*E*	*F*	...
	...	...	...	...
	...	...	...	...

We can now predict, and verify by crosses, that however many more genes, dominant or recessive, of *Drosophila melanogaster,* a species with 4 pairs of chromosomes, we test in this way, we

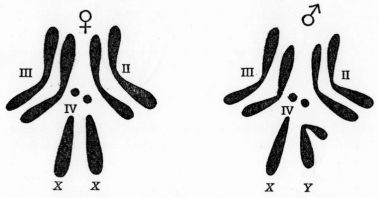

Fig. 33. The chromosome sets of female and male *Drosophila melanogaster* Meig.

shall be able to locate them on chromosome I, II, III, or IV. *The number of linkage groups is exactly the same as the number of pairs of chromosomes.*

Figure 33 depicts the 8 chromosomes, ranged in pairs, of this fly (the difference between the sexes will be studied in a later chapter). The fly itself appears in Fig. 34. The chromosomes obviously differ in size, one pair being very small. Correspondingly, in the testing of several hundred genes only a few could be assigned to one of the chromosomes. This, called the fourth

111

chromosome, was clearly the very small chromosome identified under the microscope. Here was powerful verification of the chromosome theory of heredity!

Since these pioneering studies many species of organisms with diverse chromosome numbers have been similarly examined. Thus, there are Drosophila species with 3, 4, and 5 pairs of chromosomes; in every case the number of linkage groups has been shown to equal the number of chromosome pairs. Maize,

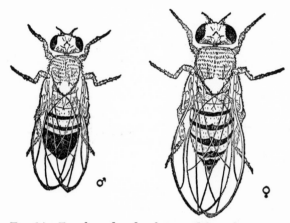

Fig. 34. Female and male of *Drosophila melanogaster.*

with 10 pairs of chromosomes, has proved to have 10 linkage groups. Snapdragons have 7 pairs of chromosomes and 7 linkage groups. Where the number of chromosomes is large it becomes more difficult to determine all the linkage groups. Much time and enormous labor will be needed before the results of the Drosophila and corn studies are matched in man, who has 24 pairs of chromosomes and for whom, experimentation being impracticable, the geneticist must rely upon complicated mathematical methods for testing for linkage of such genes as happen to be picked up in particular pedigrees.

The order of genes within the chromosome

It is thus clear that each chromosome contains a number of linked genes. Chromosomes, when they are not contracted into rods and dots, are threadlike bodies, and their duplication in cell division is always by what looks like a longitudinal, lengthwise

112

split. Soon after the true facts of cell division became known, some keen thinkers (Roux, Weismann) realized that genes (then called determiners) must be arranged in a row along the chromosome if they are to be divided or reproduced simultaneously and equally when the chromosome is duplicated. This conclusion was entirely logical, but experimental proof was still needed. As a matter of fact, the linear arrangement of genes on chromosomes was generally accepted even before the rise of modern genetics. But an added problem appeared as some investigators began to wonder whether the genes occupy *definite* positions along the chromosomes. The reader will remember that evidence was presented locating the Mendelizing factors on homologous chromosomes and that it was implicitly assumed that definite positions of the genes is a fact. This must now be proved. Proof will be obtained by following experiments of T. H. Morgan and his collaborators, who transformed a reasonable assumption arrived at by logical analysis into an experimentally demonstrated fact of great significance.

The double backcross

To understand these experiments we must go back once more to the simple Mendelian ratios. We previously studied the Mendelian backcross, noting its importance in analyzing human heredity, but its importance as a general tool in genetic analysis has not yet been discussed. Actually the backcross is a basic method in the study of linkage, as well as of many other problems. Now linkage must deal with a minimum of 2 pairs of alleles on the same chromosome pair; for this purpose the simple Mendelian backcross ($Aa \times aa$ produces $\frac{1}{2}$ Aa, $\frac{1}{2}$ aa) is obviously inadequate. We must, therefore, examine a backcross involving, first of all, 2 *independent* pairs of alleles.

Let us use a familiar example, the cross of black short-haired with white long-haired guinea pigs. The F_1 from this mating is black short-haired, these being the 2 dominant characters. This hybrid is backcrossed by breeding to the double recessive parent, the long-haired white: $BbSs \times bbss$. As we expect, the hybrid produces 4 kinds of gametes in equal proportions: BS, Bs, bS, bs. Each of these can be fertilized by (or fertilize) the gametes of the homozygous recessive parent, all of which carry bs. The result is, clearly, 4 combinations—$BSbs$, $Bsbs$, $bSbs$, $bsbs$—in equal

113

numbers, a ratio of $1:1:1:1$. Phenotypically the first type exhibits the dominant traits, black and short; the second, dominant black with recessive long; the third, dominant short with recessive white; and the fourth, the 2 recessives white and long. These 4 *phenotypes* thus directly parallel and reflect in their visible characters the *genotypes* of the gametes of the F_1 hybrid. Thus we have the 4 types of gametes (and, in parentheses, the 4 phenotypes from the backcross): B(black) S(short); B(black) s(long); b(white) S(short); b(white) s(long). From the phenotypes segregating in a backcross we can read the genic composition of the gametes of the hybrid, as the last enumeration should make abundantly clear. Moreover, the fact that the phenotypes appeared in equal numbers (ratio of $1:1:1:1$) proves that the corresponding types of gametes were produced in equal numbers. Had the experiment given us, say, 7 black-short : 1 black-long : 1 white-short : 7 white-long, we could therefore, legitimately conclude that the hybrid had produced 7 times as many gametes carrying BS or bs as gametes with Bs or bS. *Backcrossing the heterozygote (the hybrid) to the homozygous recessive tells us the relative numbers, as well as the types of gametes involved.*

We are now in a position to see that linked genes would give us similar results. For the genes A and B, representing any suitable characters, located on the same chromosome (as is indicated by writing them as a single fraction) the backcross experiment would run as follows:

$$\frac{AB}{ab} \text{ (the double heterozygote)} \times \frac{ab}{ab} \text{ (the double recessive)}$$

$$\text{RF}_2 \; \frac{1}{2}\frac{AB}{ab}, \frac{1}{2}\frac{ab}{ab} \left(\text{i.e., } 1\frac{AB}{ab}, 1\frac{AB}{ab}, 1\frac{ab}{ab}, 1\frac{ab}{ab} \right)$$

These results clearly mean that the hybrid formed only the gametes AB (linked) and ab (linked), in equal numbers. However, when such a backcross experiment was actually carried out in Drosophila with 2 pairs of alleles known to be on the same chromosome, quite surprising results were obtained (this is what has been repeatedly alluded to as the "special features" of linkage). Similar findings had, indeed, previously resulted from studies with sweet peas, without their being properly under-

114

stood. In these fly crosses, most of the RF_2 individuals fell into the expected classes, equal proportions of the phenotypes AB and ab (genotypically $\frac{AB}{ab}$ and $\frac{ab}{ab}$). But a certain number of the progeny had the 2 unexpected and, for linkage, non-permissible, combinations, the phenotypes Ab and aB (genotypically $\frac{Ab}{ab}$ and $\frac{aB}{ab}$), the 2 aberrant classes appearing in equal numbers. Linkage had been broken in a definite percentage of cases.

Break of linkage or crossing over

Let us consider an actual example of linkage and breakage of linkage, involving recessive traits. We shall use the genes for 2 Mendelizing traits, genes which, from linkage experiments of the type already described, were known to lie on the so-called second chromosome of Drosophila (one of the large pairs in Fig. 33). One is a recessive allele causing black body color (b); its dominant (B) controls the so-called wild-type, yellowish brown body with black cross bands, giving a grayish impression when seen at a little distance. The second gene, vg, also recessive, reduces the wings to small stumps, called vestigial wings; its dominant allele Vg stands for normal.

At this point another simplifying symbol can be introduced. One of the alleles of a pair typically controls the normal character of the fly, rabbit, mouse, or other organism we are using. We can denote any and all such genes controlling the normal or wild type by $+$ (plus). Thus, $\frac{+}{b}$ would be the same as Bb in our previous notation, and $\frac{+}{vg}$ is the same as $\frac{Vg}{vg}$. If many wild-type genes are considered simultaneously and it is necessary to make clear which particular one is meant in a specific case, we use $+^b$ or $+^{vg}$ for the normal allele of b or vg, respectively. A fly homozygous for both the second chromosome recessives listed above would be $\frac{b\,vg}{b\,vg}$; the homozygous wild-type fly, $\frac{+\,+}{+\,+}$ or $\frac{+^b\,+^{vg}}{+^b\,+^{vg}}$; the F_1 hybrid, $\frac{+\,+}{b\,vg}$. As in other notations, the fraction indicates a pair of homologous chromosomes.

115

Now let us backcross a phenotypically black vestigial, genotypically doubly homozygous female to an F_1 male, phenotypically wild type and genotypically heterozygous for both of these genes. In symbols the cross is (note the customary practice of listing the female parent first)

$$\frac{b \, vg}{b \, vg} \; \times \; \frac{+\,+}{b \, vg}$$

The backcross progeny include, as we expect where linkage is complete, equal numbers of the parental types, normal and black-vestigial, or

$$\frac{1}{2} \frac{b \, vg}{b \, vg}, \quad \frac{1}{2} \frac{+\,+}{b \, vg}$$

Figure 35 illustrates the cross and progeny in terms of chromosomes, and the old notation of capital letters for the dominant wild type is still used in this and the following figures. In the first row are the parents—normal female and black vestigial male —and, below them, their mature sex cells with only the second chromosome drawn, containing the linked black and vestigial genes and their normal alleles. The chromosome containing the normal genes is drawn black; the one with the recessives, white. The third row depicts cells of the F_1 hybrid. The next row pictures the flies used for the backcross, the double recessive female and F_1 male. Below them are their mature gametes, of which 2 types are produced by the hybrid. Arrows indicate the 2 possible kinds of fertilization. Resulting progeny are shown in the bottom row: equal proportions of the 2 parental types. Although only one sex is drawn, an equal number of the other sex occurs. Half the individuals of both sexes are black-vestigial; half are wild type. Linkage of the 2 genes within the chromosome is, in fact, complete in this case.

When, however, a comparable backcross was made, this time with an F_1 *female* instead of a male, giving

$$\frac{b \, vg}{+\,+} \; \times \; \frac{b \, vg}{b \, vg}$$

a quite different result was obtained. As in the preceding experiment, the majority of the offspring were of the parental types,

116

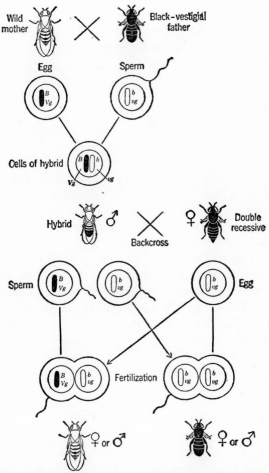

Fig. 35. Diagram of the backcross of a male, himself the offspring of a cross normal × black-vestigial, with a homozygous black-vestigial female. (*First two rows*) The original parents and their sex cells, with only the second chromosome containing black-vestigial or their wild-type alleles represented. Black indicates the normal chromosome (*B* and *Vg*); white, the chromosome containing the 2 mutant alleles *b* and *vg*. (*Third row*) Cells of the hybrids, (*fourth row*) the hybrid male to be backcrossed to the pure double recessive parental type, (*fifth row*) sex cells of the hybrid, (*sixth row*) the 2 types of fertilization and the resulting 2 backcross types.

black-vestigial and normal; but, in addition, the unexpected and illegitimate types, black–not vestigial and not black–vestigial, appeared. Linkage between black and vestigial had here been broken, and the 2 pairs of alleles behaved in a part of the offspring as though they were located in different chromosomes. Such breakage was, be it noted, incomplete, for the number of unexpected types was smaller than the total of expected ones. Linkage had been incomplete, had been broken in the heterozygous female, though it was not broken in the heterozygous male. Figure 36 presents this case in a diagram (see legend).

At this juncture it must be stressed that this difference between heterozygous female and heterozygous male as to whether linkage is complete is a special feature of Drosophila and definitely not a general phenomenon. For the discussion we could welcome the difference, for it permits describing complete linkage and breakage of linkage in so-called reciprocal backcrosses, differing only in the sex of the heterozygous individual. This property of Drosophila contributed in some way to the original discovery of this phenomenon, simplifying its analysis. There are, however, plant and animal species in which breakage of linkage occurs only during gamete formation in males, and there are many other species in which such breakage occurs in both sexes; the reason behind the existence of these different types, we must frankly admit, is as yet quite unclear. In what follows we shall restrict ourselves to the Drosophila type, because of its comparative simplicity.

It is by now readily seen that breakage of linkage must, in our example, have involved some kind of exchange of genes between a pair of homologous chromosomes during gametogenesis (= formation of gametes) in the heterozygous female. One of the second chromosomes of this female contained the genes $B\,Vg$, its partner having $b\,vg$. In order to produce the unexpected backcross phenotypes black body–normal wings and wild-type color–vestigial wings, the chromosome segment containing B must have "crossed over" to the segment of the homologue containing vg, and the segment with b must have joined with the segment of the partner having Vg. (This is indicated in Fig. 36 in the row "Crossover Eggs.") Thus the unexpected, the crossover gametes bearing the combinations $B\,vg$ and $b\,Vg$ could be formed, along with gametes having chromosomes like

118

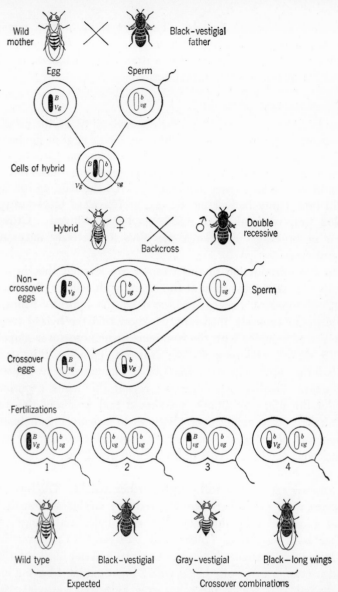

Fig. 36. Diagram of backcross with the hybrid female × double recessive male. First three rows like Fig. 35. (*Fourth row*) Mother and father of backcross, (*fifth and sixth rows*) the 4 types of eggs of the F₁ female and the sperm of the father, (*seventh row*) the 4 types of fertilization with the non-crossover and crossover eggs, (*eighth row*) the expected and the crossover phenotypes (they appear in both sexes; in the drawing either females or males are shown, to which no meaning is attached).

those of the parent female. The formation of two comple-
mentary kinds of unexpected gametes argues that *crossing over*
—this is the technical term—results from an exchange of material
between homologous chromosomes.

The crossover percentage

In our experiment we found the unexpected types, the products
of crossing over in the second chromosomes of eggs of the heterozygous female, only in smaller numbers than the parental combinations; were genes in different chromosomes involved, we
should, of course, expect like numbers. Of the RF_2, 40.75% were
wild type (gray body–long wings), 40.75% were black-vestigial,
9.25% gray-vestigial, and 9.25% black–long-winged. Crossing
over or breakage of linkage was thus a relatively uncommon
occurrence.

In the introduction to this chapter we learned that in a recessive backcross the ratio of the phenotypes tells us directly the
ratio of types of gametes produced by the hybrid. From the
data in our example, therefore, we know that the hybrid formed
4 types of gametes with the frequencies: non-crossover gametes,
$B\,Vg$, 40.75%, and $b\,vg$, 40.75%; crossover gametes, $B\,vg$, 9.25%,
and $b\,Vg$, 9.25%. In sum, 18.5% of the gametes were crossover
gametes. Further, whenever we repeat this same experiment
under the same conditions, we should find precisely this same
percentage of crossing over (both as to crossover gametes and
backcross phenotypes) between the second chromosome genes
black and vestigial. This uniformity of results is, we shall see,
an important fact.

Another experiment will lead to further insight. The foregoing
crosses were made between 2 hereditary strains so constituted
that 1 carried both dominants (normal color and wings), the
other both recessives (black and vestigial). Crossover individuals were therefore black–not vestigial and not black–vestigial.
But we can just as easily begin with 2 other stocks, 1 having black
body but long wings, the other gray body but vestigial wings,
like the crossover individuals of the preceding crosses. By crossing these 2 hereditary lines we shall obtain an F_1 hybrid with
the second chromosomes $\dfrac{B\,vg}{b\,Vg}$. Now when crossing over takes

120

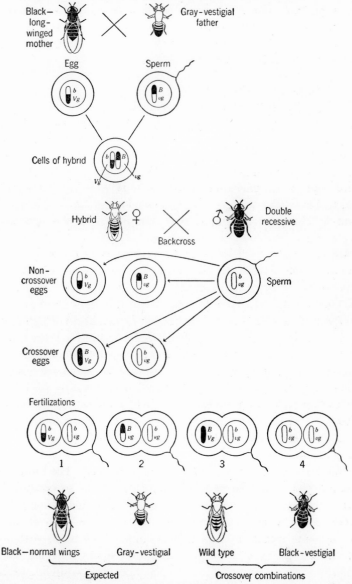

FIG. 37. Like Fig. 36, but parents are black with normal wings and gray with vestigial wings. Therefore the normal sex cells of the hybrid contain black-normal and gray-vestigial, but the crossover eggs contain black-vestigial and gray-normal, respectively. Correspondingly the non-crossover flies look like the original parents, but the crossover flies are now black-vestigial and wild type. (See note about the sexes in Fig. 36.)

121

place between the 2 homologous chromosomes, the crossover gametes will be *b vg* and *B Vg*. What were in the first experiment the linked and expected combinations are here the unexpected ones involving breakage of linkage or crossing over, and vice versa. What about the frequencies of the 4 classes of progeny, the 2 non-crossover classes black—not vestigial and vestigial—not black, and the 2 crossover classes normal and black-vestigial? We shall find exactly the same frequency as in the preceding experiment: 81.5% non-crossovers and 18.5% crossovers, irrespective of the fact that what were non-crossover phenotypes in the first experiment are here crossover phenotypes. In brief, the frequency of crossing over is constant for the 2 pairs of alleles studied, and is wholly independent of whether 2 dominants, 1 dominant and 1 recessive, or any other combination occurs in a particular chromosome. The percentage of crossing over in a double heterozygote is a fixed property of the 2 genes located on a given chromosome. Figure 37 illustrates this experiment, paralleling Fig. 36 for the first experiment.

The evident next step in this analysis is to determine the crossover values between other gene couples known, from experiments of the kind previously described, to be located on the same chromosome. All such tests give the same sort of segregation in backcrosses, a majority of progeny being non-crossovers, half of this group with each original combination of linked genes, and a smaller number being crossovers, half of these with each of the 2 possible changed combinations. Moreover, the frequency of crossing over is always typical of the genes used, though not the same as in our experiment. Thus, 2 genes, call them *a* and *b*, in the first chromosome always give 3% crossovers; the genes *m* and *n* in the third chromosome give 12%, etc. The crossover values for a given couple of genes may be anywhere from 1% (occasionally less) to 50% (note that 50% crossing over would lead to the same results as free recombination, a gametic ratio of $1 : 1 : 1 : 1$).

Crossing over and map distance

What lies behind these facts? The answer to this question was discovered by thinking out what could be happening in the chromosomes when the exchange of genes occurs. Two possibilities are apparent. A pair of alleles (one could conceive) might somehow leave its place in its chromosome and change places with its allele in the homologous chromosome. Alternatively, entire chromosome segments including their contained genes could be exchanged. This would require that at some time before the reduction division, when the homologous chromosomes are paired side by side, a break must occur in each of them at matched points between the "loci" or sites occupied by the 2 pairs of alleles. The 2 pieces thus broken off would then be exchanged. And, as a matter of fact, cytologists had previously seen that at certain stages the pairs of chromosomes actually formed crosslike figures, called "chiasmata" (sing., chiasma), which could be interpreted as visible evidence of an exchange of segments. This idea, the exchange of entire sections between homologous chromosomes, turned out to be correct, and it has since been shown to be a demonstrable fact. The details are a bit more complicated than has been indicated, and for an understanding of advanced genetics such details are very important. But for this elementary presentation I shall avoid any possibility of confusing the reader by simply sticking to the essential facts needed to grasp the relation of genes and chromosomes, merely noting that matters are being somewhat simplified. What happens in crossing over, in this simplified scheme, is shown by Fig. 38. A pair of chromosomes is drawn in synapsis; that from one parent of the hybrid is black, and has the dominant alleles A and B; that from the other parent is white, with the recessive alleles a and b. The 2 homologues then twist about one another, forming a chiasma, and subsequently break, possibly as a result of the torsion. After breakage the broken ends reunite, but in the "wrong" way, so that each chromosome has exchanged a black for a white segment. The segments, of course, contain genes; thus the crossed-over chromosomes are marked by the gene combinations Ab and aB: Crossing over, thus, is seen to be an exchange of chromosome segments between homologues, the break occurring between the loci of the 2 pairs of alleles which, in effect, label the sections of chromosomes. (May I repeat that the details are a little more complicated and hint at this occasion that the omitted complication explains the necessity of 2 maturation divisions?)

Let us look further at this matter of the point of breakage of the chromosome. In Fig. 38 this point lies at the middle of the chromosome. There is no apparent reason why it should actually occur there in preference to any other spot along the chromosome. Indeed, microscopic investigation reveals that chiasmata, which somehow reflect the locus of breakage, appear at many different positions along the elongated, threadlike chromosomes. From such observations it was concluded that the point at which a break occurs is a matter of chance. If genes have specific posi-

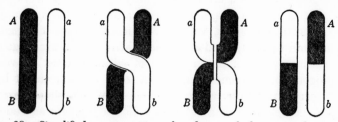

Fig. 38. Simplified representation of exchange of chromosomal segments between a pair of homologous chromosomes via chiasma formation and crossing over between the pairs of alleles *Aa* and *Bb*. (The actual process is more complicated, but the details are not needed for the understanding of the simplest facts.)

tions, definite loci on a chromosome, a break should be more probable between 2 genes which are apart than between 2 genes close together, provided only that the likelihood of breakage at every point on the chromosome is the same as for breakage at all other points. Assume, merely to visualize this situation, that along a chromosome are 100 equally spaced points at which breakage can take place. If 1 gene lies between points 20 and 21 and a second between points 50 and 51, there are 30 possibilities out of 100 for a break between them; in other words, the probability that a break on this chromosome will come between the 2 genes is 30%. In contrast, if 1 gene is located between points 20 and 21 and the other between points 22 and 23 there are only 2 chances in 100 of a break between them, or the probability of such a break is only 2%. The converse is also true. If the actual number of breaks, the number of crossovers between 2 pairs of alleles, is known, we can from that information determine what distance on the chromosome separates the 2 genes. If experimental test finds 30% crossovers between genes *A* and *B*

124

but only 2% between *C* and *D*, it follows that *A* and *B* are 15 times as far apart as are *C* and *D*. *Crossover frequencies are a measure of the distance separating 2 genes on a chromosome,* always assuming equal chance of breakage at any point. Confirmation arises from the constancy of crossover values for any 2 given genes on a particular chromosome, as shown by repeated experiments. Demonstration thus proves the logical deduction of earlier thinkers: Genes do occupy definite positions on the chromosomes.

The measure of distance between 2 genes in terms of crossover percentages is clearly not an absolute one. We could not express such distance as 30 centimeters or millimeters or microns. In our description we assumed 100 breaking points merely to be able to express the probability for a particular break in terms of percentages. All measurements really rest upon arbitrary but useful scales. Centigrade degrees are obtained by dividing the expansion of a mercury column from the freezing point to the boiling point of water into 100 sections; the meter is 1/40,000,000th of the circumference of the earth along the meridian through the poles. In a similar fashion, the unit for determining spacing of genes along chromosomes was taken to be 1% crossing over. In this way the black and vestigial loci, the sites of the black and vestigial genes on the second chromosome of *Drosophila melanogaster,* were determined to be 18.5 units apart.

Mapping the entire chromosome

A crossover experiment with 2 genes gives us information on the distance separating them, but it tells nothing about whether the 2 are near one end of the chromosome, near the middle, etc. How is localization to be made more precise? We may continue to consider the problem of the positions of black and vestigial on the second chromosome of Drosophila. Experiments determining comparable localizations of genes turned up another recessive on the second chromosome, a factor changing eye color from the normal red to purple. A typical backcross crossover test was then made for the 2 genes black and purple; 6% crossing over was found, and the distance black-purple determined as 6 units. Next a crossover test was carried out with vestigial and purple; this gave a distance for vestigial-purple of 12.5 units.

Since the distance black-vestigial was already known to be 18.5 units, the purple locus must be between black and vestigial, thus:

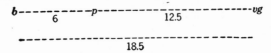

A fourth gene in the second chromosome was found to change eye shape from the normal roundness to an irregular bean shape; it was called Lobe (*L*) and was dominant to the wild-type allele *l*. Lobe in crossover experiments with black proved to be 23.5 units from black; similar experiments with Lobe and purple gave the distance between them as 17.5 units; and experiments with Lobe and vestigial fixed their distance at 5 units. The order and spacing of the 4 loci on the chromosome must therefore be

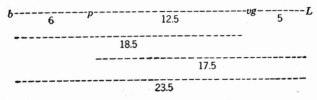

Other genes can be tested by the same method; they will be found to lie between 2 genes previously localized, or to the left of the first one, or to the right of the last one. A gene giving 3% crossovers with *vg* and 2% with Lobe must be located between the two. A gene giving 5% crossovers with Lobe but 10% with vestigial must be 5 units to the right of Lobe (28.5 units from *b* beyond Lobe). One giving 4% crossovers with black and 10% with purple must be situated 4 units to the left of black. If a large number of genes are available for testing, one will eventually turn up which in all combinations lies farthest to the left. This locus can then be taken as the zero point, and the positions of all other genes reckoned by their distances from it. When relatively full data were obtained for the second chromosome, for example, many genes were found to be left of black up to a distance of 48.5 units; none could be shown to lie farther left. In the finished map of this chromosome, then, black is assigned the locus 48.5; this puts purple at 54.5, vestigial at 67, and Lobe at 72. The other chromosomes of Drosophila have been similarly mapped, so that each known pair of alleles can

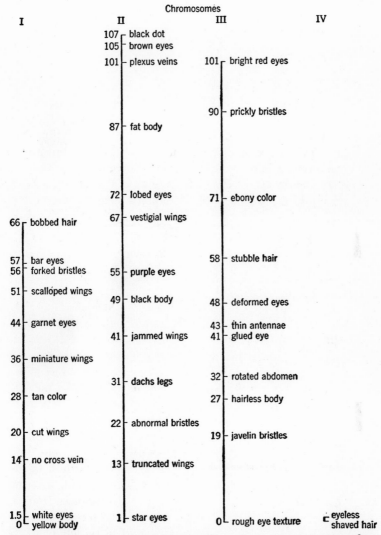

Chromosomes

I	II	III	IV

I

66 ⎰ bobbed hair

57 ⎱ bar eyes
56 ⎱ forked bristles

51 ⊢ scalloped wings

44 ⊢ garnet eyes

36 ⊢ miniature wings

28 ⊢ tan color

20 ⊢ cut wings

14 ⊢ no cross vein

1.5 ⎰ white eyes
0 ⎱ yellow body

II

107 ⎰ black dot
105 ⎱ brown eyes

101 ⊢ plexus veins

87 ⊢ fat body

72 ⊢ lobed eyes

67 ⊢ vestigial wings

55 ⊢ purple eyes

49 ⊢ black body

41 ⊢ jammed wings

31 ⊢ dachs legs

22 ⊢ abnormal bristles

13 ⊢ truncated wings

1 ⊢ star eyes

III

101 ⊢ bright red eyes

90 ⊢ prickly bristles

71 ⊢ ebony color

58 ⊢ stubble hair

48 ⊢ deformed eyes

43 ⎰ thin antennae
41 ⎱ glued eye

32 ⊢ rotated abdomen

27 ⊢ hairless body

19 ⊢ javelin bristles

0 ⎰ rough eye texture

IV

⎰ eyeless
⎱ shaved hair

FIG. 39. A chromosome map of *Drosophila melanogaster* containing only a small part of the mutant loci. The names for the phenotypes are given not always in the technical language but rather so as to convey an idea of the visible effect. The numbers correspond to the distances in crossover units, omitting decimals.

127

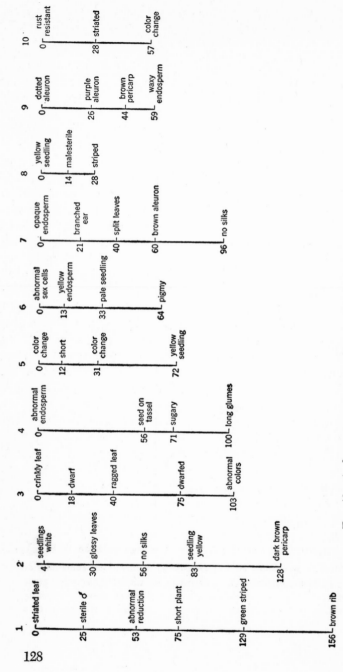

Fig. 40. A chromosome map for maize, comparable to Fig. 39 for Drosophila.

be described by its location; for example, black (*b*) 2—48.5 (the chromosome number is conventionally cited first, followed by the locus), and yellow (*y*) 1—0.0. Yellow is the locus at the extreme left end of the first chromosome. Such chromosome maps, with only a fraction of the known loci included, are represented in Fig. 39, with descriptive names for the genes rather than those found in genetic work. No reader will be surprised that the observed lengths of the 4 chromosomes check with the lengths of their genetic maps.

The critical reader will recognize that these maps, based as they are on the assumption that crossover breaks occur exactly as frequently at one point on the chromosomes as at any other, will reflect the true distance relations of loci only if this assumption can be shown to be valid. If some sections of the chromosome break more readily than others, the positions of the loci will be distorted from their real sites, though the order of loci will be unchanged. We shall return to this problem later on, for we shall find that there are methods for comparing actual positions with those determined by crossover methods.

The chromosomes of many organisms have been mapped since these tools were introduced. Some maps are impressively long and well-filled, as those for various Drosophila species; others, though further from completion, are quite satisfactory, as for maize (Fig. 40); those for species like snapdragon and sweet pea are useful but much less detailed; and many, including those for most mammals, among them man, are only fragmentary. The genuinely astonishing thing, however, is that mapping has never produced any freakish results, despite the enormous number of numerical relations which must tally precisely to prove the principle. It was a proud exhibit that the geneticists of Cornell University presented to an international assemblage of their fellow investigators in 1932, toward the end of a period of research devoted extensively to such problems: hundreds of strains of corn representing the many sets of alleles, grown in their due and proper positions in beds simulating the sizes and shapes of the chromosomes of Indian corn!

Mutation

The knowledge of genetic and cytological facts acquired by the reader up to this point makes it imperative to study now a basic and important phenomenon heretofore pushed aside to simplify our analysis. We have constantly used for the various problems of Mendelian inheritance crosses between strains, varieties differing in one or more pairs of Mendelian alleles. These were referred to as horticultural varieties, strains, lines, races, etc., without offering any explanation of their origin. For example, it was stated that almost a thousand genic differences are known in Drosophila. How did these reach the experimenter's laboratory? Were they somehow discovered in nature and collected? Did they originate under the investigator's eyes? Were they produced at will?

General information

In earlier chapters reference was made to Darwin's theory of evolution; it was pointed out that this explanation of evolution as the result of selection of hereditary variants was, in part, based upon the experience of the plant and animal breeder. Darwin argued that the domesticated breeds of horses, dogs, pigs, sweet peas, chrysanthemums, etc., must have been derived by man from wild ancestors of these animals and plants, which were domesticated and bred. Examination of the wild forms probably ancestral to the domesticated types discloses that the different wild species are rather uniform, without conspicuous variation. One may think of the wolf, coyote, or fox as wild species ancestral to dogs and compare the similarity of wolves to the scores of extremely divergent breeds of dogs; or one may contrast the uniformity of wild boars to the many breeds of

130

domestic swine. How did this diversity originate, after domestication of the wild ancestral forms? Darwin believed that the breeder created this diversity by watching for variations in his flocks, herds, and crop plants, then selecting the most promising variants for breeding and continuing this selection until a stable new breed or line was established. In a general way Darwin was right, but we now better understand the meaning of variation and selection. One aspect of the problem has been discussed previously, where it was pointed out that variation can be produced by the breeder by crossing different races found in nature or under domestication. The example concerned British and Asiatic pigs, the crosses resulting in Mendelian segregation. Such a segregating F_2 population, especially where many allelic differences are involved, clearly includes a very great deal of variation. Selection from such a population, we saw, simply means the isolation of new homozygous gene combinations, which become the new breed produced by the breeder. This procedure we may call selection of variants because the breeder selected what Darwin called variants, bred these, and repeated the procedure until he obtained the desired type. In the light of present-day knowledge, he carried out a Mendelian recombination experiment.

This, however, is only part of the story. It seems very unlikely that the bowlegs of the dachshund, piebald patterns of cattle, Angora hair of dogs or guinea pigs, or abnormal jaws of the bulldog or pug were collected from existing varieties and crossed into the chosen ones. Darwin himself was well aware that such hereditary traits appear occasionally as freaks, as it were, in one or a few abnormal individuals in a completely homogeneous herd, flock, or flower bed. He also knew that these sudden or "single" variations—"sports" the breeders called them —immediately bred true for the new character. He knew that in plants even a single twig or shoot, outgrowth of a solitary bud, might suddenly change its type (bud variation or bud sport) and this new type breed true. His well-known example was the origin of the nectarine as a single bud variation on a peach tree. The most famous instance of a sport among domestic animals is the Ancon (or Otter) sheep, a sheep with legs like those of a dachshund, a trait that appeared in a single individual born in a New England herd more than a century ago. Bred to normal, the variant could be extracted in the F_2 as what we know now to be a Mendelian segregant. A breed of Ancon sheep was therefore established, and it flourished for some years, for farmers liked a sheep unable to leap over fences. Many similar, though rare, occurrences had come to the attention of animal breeders, seed growers, and horticulturists before the rising science of genetics analyzed the phenomenon.

The terms "single variation" and "sport" have disappeared from our vocabulary. A hereditary change produced in a single step is called a "mutant," and the process producing a mutant is "mutation." Remembering the facts of Mendelian heredity and its chromosomal basis, we may expect—and rightly so—that mutation is a process affecting chromosomes and genes. We shall restrict ourselves for the present to study of gene mutations, though it is possible that a whole chromosome, or even more than one, can change so that the product is a mutant.

Gene mutation

We have seen that at different and definite points on the chromosomes there are structures called genes, whatever this name for a tiny chromosome segment, separable from its neighbors by crossing over, may mean. Each gene must be in charge of controlling or producing a chain of chemical reactions which in the end determines the visible character. It is here quietly assumed that all the other genes simultaneously carry out their proper work and that the environment remains ever the same (these assumptions will be discussed later). For the results of a Mendelian cross to be reproducible time after time these genes must remain constant; this means that before each division of a chromosome each gene must fashion its own complete likeness. We do not yet know how this process of *self-duplication of the gene* is accomplished, but we are certain that it must always take place. In view of these circumstances, we should expect the hereditary nature of an organism to remain completely unchanged, constant through all the generations. But if, as we have just seen, changes occur by mutation, the new mutants being themselves hereditarily constant and invariable from their first appearance, it is clear that mutation is a change within a gene, perhaps an error at the time of self-duplication. Since the gene repeatedly forms its own likeness at the time of duplication,

132

the new and changed gene, which we call the mutated gene, must necessarily start reproducing *its* likeness. In other words, the change in the gene by mutation, the mutant gene, is hereditary. Gene mutation immediately produces a new hereditary element.

Now let us consider mutation in terms of Mendelian gene theory. We may think, for example, of the locus, the point, on chromosome II in Drosophila which we determined in the preceding chapter as the locus $+^{vg}$ 2–67.0. This is a gene necessary for the formation of a normal wing. A mutation at this locus would change the gene into a different one which so controls development that a vestigial wing appears: $+^{vg}$ has mutated to vg; further, since vg is only a changed $+^{vg}$, it follows that $+^{vg}$ and vg are alleles, different conditions of one and the same gene. The same rules apply to all loci. A mutation produces an allele of the mutated locus, and the new mutant must show simple Mendelian behavior when crossed to the original form.

This insight at once answers the question which started this discussion: How do the various strains used in our Mendelian experiments originate? The fact that each of them exhibits simple Mendelian relations with the original wild type proves that all originated by mutations. Vestigial was a recessive mutant of its wild-type allele at the proper locus; so were black, purple, and all the others we mentioned. Lobe was a dominant mutant at its locus. All the 1000 dominant or recessive mutants at different loci, used to establish the chromosome maps, similarly arose by mutation. What we previously labeled strains were actually individual mutants that had originated suddenly and been isolated by the experimenter as true-breeding homozygotes. *Mutation is the means whereby new hereditary types are produced.*

We have said that these mutants were isolated by the experimenter; this description is related to a further interesting fact. In every organism the chromosomes occur as paired homologues, 2 of each kind. Each gene is therefore present as 2. Mutation could occur in 1 or both, the first making the individual heterozygous and the second making it homozygous for the mutant character. In reality mutations originally occur in only 1 of the homologous chromosomes, in heterozygous condition. This raises a problem: How can the mutants be found, and how can it be proved that mutation has actually taken place? Clearly, no dif-

133

ficulties arise when dominant mutants are involved. If a type of animal or plant, inbred for generations, preferably by brother-sister matings or self-fertilization, remains true-breeding, the sudden appearance of one or a few new hereditary types indicates a mutation. A cross to the original form may show the new form to be a Mendelian dominant, which must be a mutant since the dominant could not have been previously overlooked. Many mutants have been isolated in just this way in practical and experimental work. But in the case of recessive mutants further precautions are needed. We have already learned that a recessive can be carried in heterozygous condition through many generations and become manifest only when 2 heterozygotes chance to mate and the homozygote segregates out. Thus, the appearance of what may look like a recessive mutant in a line carried along without proper checks may in fact be the segregation of a recessive already present. Methods are available to avoid this error. If brother-sister matings are continued for many generations, the probability that recessives can remain hidden by failing to meet another heterozygote at fertilization becomes smaller and smaller; finally, the line can be judged free of hidden recessives. Moreover, geneticists have devised some rather complicated methods for removing all heterozygosity from all chromosomes, and such undoubtedly homozygous strains will reveal recessive mutants reliably. Such precautions, however, are necessary only when experiments aim at a study of mutation frequency. After all, any recessive allele must once upon a time have originated as a mutant.

Mutation in sex and body cells

Let us look a little more deeply into the origin of mutants. If mutants originate in 1 allele or a pair of alleles at any point on a chromosome, it is safe to assume that mutation may occur in any cell. We have previously noted the distinction between the unbroken line of sex cells and the body. If a mutation occurs in a body cell of an organism during development, the mutant character, if dominant, will be visible in all cells derived from the mutated one, and a patch or mosaic spot of different character will be formed. But can we be sure that this is a mutation and not a chance effect, a purely phenotypical character having nothing to do with the chromosomes and genes? In animals no such decision can, in fact, be made. But in plants a different situation may exist. For we may be able to propagate the changed portion as a cutting, and it may turn out (subject to certain features of plant development) that flowers, pollen, and seeds will be formed from the abnormal patch. If an actual mutation had originally occurred in the body cell, the new character or—it is better to say—the underlying mutant gene will be inherited. Body cells are called somatic cells (*soma* = body), as contrasted to the sex cells. We might therefore say that we had found a somatic mutation which could be propagated. As a rule, however, the mutants we study originate in the sex cells. If a dominant mutant appears at some locus before the maturation divisions, 2 of the mature gametes will contain it and, in favorable circumstances, i.e., with successful fertilizations, the new mutant will appear in 2 individuals. But sex cells undergo many divisions before the reduction divisions. A mutant gene appearing at an earlier time during this series of divisions will therefore be distributed to a larger number of gametes, and a correspondingly higher number of mutants will appear among the offspring. Mutations may also occur immediately before fertilization, so that only a single mutant individual results.

A recessive mutant in a somatic cell will not be evident if, as is usual, only 1 of a pair of genes has mutated. Similarly, a mutation in a sex cell will not be seen in the heterozygous offspring. If only 1 or 2 gametes contain the recessive mutant, it may be lost if the gamete fails to fertilize or be fertilized. An earlier mutation, producing many heterozygous gametes, affords a better likelihood that a number of F_1 individuals will be heterozygous, and this in turn increases the probability that from a number of haphazard matings some of the F_2 will include ¼ homozygous recessive mutants.

It is interesting to consider the chances for discovering mutants in man. A woman produces about 500 fertilizable eggs during her fertile years. Millions of sperm are produced by the male, but only, say, 4 eggs and sperm cells unite for the production of children. The probability that mutants will be preserved is thus very slim, if mutations are rare events, and the chance for recovering new recessive mutants after the mating of 2 newly heterozygous individuals is still slighter. Nevertheless, a number of rather reliable records of dominant mutants are

135

known for characters which are so conspicuous that they could not have been overlooked. A famous example is the appearance by mutation of a skin abnormality in which horny excrescences and spines are produced all over the body. Recessive mutants, too, can be discovered in man, but doing so requires a genetic situation we shall study in the next chapter.

Experimental mutation and types of mutants

In the reader's mind a question has, no doubt, arisen: What causes genes, known to remain constant, to mutate occasionally? To the riddle of mutation continually occurring in nature, in flower beds, in experimental plots or cages, in the bottles in which Drosophila are reared—so-called spontaneous mutation—it must be confessed that a satisfactory answer has not yet been found. The influence of cosmic rays has been suggested, but these rays have proved not to be sufficiently powerful. The minute vibrations taking place in all matter under the influence of temperature differences, which might break chemical bonds in the molecule or part of a molecule or group of molecules called genes, have been proposed as causes. Also suggested are mechanical or chemical errors in the duplication of a gene which result in a somewhat altered edition of the old type. If we knew what a gene actually is, we should also know what mutation is—and we could just as well reverse this statement. But, though the causes of spontaneous mutation are still unknown, it is certain that mutation can be induced experimentally. The most efficient method is the irradiation of sex cells (in Drosophila by irradiating whole flies containing sex cells) with X-rays; the stronger the dose applied, the higher the number of mutations produced. One can then say that X-rays increase the small rate of spontaneous mutations; this spontaneous rate is in the neighborhood of 1 in 100,000 individuals, though strains of Drosophila, as well as snapdragons, are known which have much higher rates. All other radiations, including gamma rays, neutrons, and ultraviolet light, have a similar, though smaller, effect. Mutations can also be produced by heat shocks and poisons. One of the poisons, mustard gas, is as effective as X-rays. Many details have been discovered in experiments on production of mutations which will one day help us to understand the process of mutation.

Some facts with bearing on different problems of genetics will be studied below.

Going back once more to the localization of the genes in the chromosomes in Drosophila, we can now see that all the different hereditary strains or types used were mutants. This work actually began in the laboratory with the breeding of the wild type of Drosophila, captured in the field. Each female fly in the breeding bottles lays 200–300 eggs, and a new generation hatches, at 25° C., every 10 days; thus not less than 1400 generations with millions and millions of flies have been bred since Drosophila became the "guinea pig" of geneticists. What this figure means can best be appreciated by contrasting it with the number of generations of man since the dawn of history in Egypt—less than 200 generations. From all those generations of Drosophila some 1000 mutants were isolated; nobody can say how many appeared, except by calculating from the total number of flies studied in all laboratories in the world—a scarcely reliable figure. These mutants, a few of which are sketched in Fig. 41 (see legend), affect all parts of the fly: color of eyes, body, hair; number and presence or absence of particular bristles; length, shape, thickness, stiffness of bristles; size and shape of body; form and finer features of eyes; segmentation of the body; size, shape, texture, completeness, even presence of wings; presence, structure, and shape of antennae and their parts; structure, shape, hairiness of legs; structure of mouth parts; color of testes; structural detail of certain parts of the internal male sex organs; physiological traits, like resistance to ether; replacement of antennae by legs, of wings by halteres, of halteres by wings, or wings by legs. Though more mutants have been found in Drosophila than in any other organism, it is evident that all observers who have worked with any species of plant or animal for some time have found mutations. The nature of these mutants can be seen in all the varieties known to horticulturists and plant and animal breeders—hundreds of color varieties of flowering plants and color and hair types of mice, guinea pigs, dogs, rabbits, horses, all of which must have arisen by mutations, since they reveal 1-gene Mendelian differences in crosses. This conclusion recalls our earlier discussion of the origin of domestic varieties by the crossing and selecting of new Mendelian recombinations. It is now

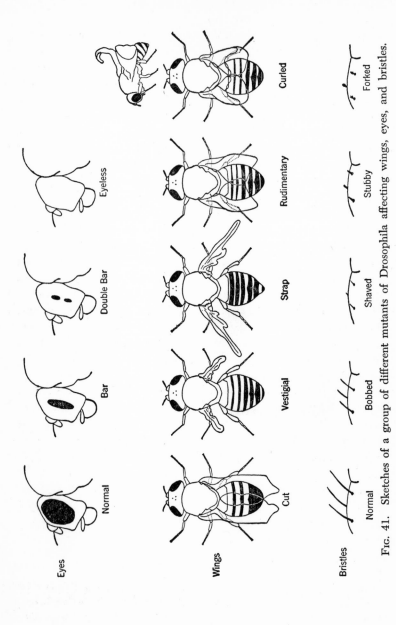

FIG. 41. Sketches of a group of different mutants of Drosophila affecting wings, eyes, and bristles.

understood that another feature of successful breeding is the discovery and isolation of new mutants.

Role of mutation in nature; mutation and evolution

But what happens in nature? Do the mutations of Drosophila or mice or rats occur only in our breeding bottles and cages? Is the so-called wild type of Drosophila, the gray (or, better, "agouti") mouse or rat or guinea pig, as found in nature, completely constant? These questions lead to an appraisal of the role of mutations in nature. And in fact the same mutants occur in nature as in the laboratory. It is rarely that a mutant is found in a collection of wild Drosophila. But if these wild flies are bred, mutants appear in the second generation which are identical to those found in experimental bottles. This suggests that mutants occur in nature but cannot establish themselves in homozygous condition. Why is this? Because the majority of these mutants are less strong, less viable, less fertile than the wild type and are therefore wiped out in the competition for food and mates or in the changing cycle of the environment. But they may be carried in heterozygous condition, as long as the wild-type heterozygote is as viable as the wild-type homozygote. This extermination of the less fit is, of course, what Darwin called selection in the struggle for existence or survival of the fittest. Study of mutation thus leads again to the problem of evolution.

Let us imagine the following situation: In a large population of insects living in a particular area a stock of many recessive mutants is carried in the heterozygous condition, whereas the homozygous mutants are unable to compete successfully. Among these mutants may be one for the reduction of wings. By migration or some chance event, the homozygous mutant, otherwise doomed, comes to live inside an anthill or on a windswept island. At once its defect, the inability to fly, becomes an advantage: The individual has found a proper "niche" to which it was "preadapted." This means that evolution does not proceed in such a way that a form invading a new environment or faced with a new set of living conditions to which it is not fitted begins to mutate; that the better-adapted mutants survive more readily and give rise to other new mutants, some of which are still better adapted to the new conditions, until, by selection, a well-adapted type develops. The actual process is, rather, this: A population always carries along an array of mutants, protected by heterozygosity (sometimes also by selective neutrality or indifference or even by the complicated workings of chance under definite conditions). When a new niche is occupied, voluntarily or not, those mutants which chance to be better fitted to the new conditions will have the advantage, will be selected to survive. The new type is selected by the environment from among "preadapted" mutants and combinations of mutants in the original population.

These few remarks illustrate how the problems of evolution require knowledge of the phenomenon of mutation, for this is the only known process of hereditary change which can provide material for evolution. Contributions are also made by knowledge of the viability of mutants under various conditions, of their distribution in populations, of their preadaptive qualities, and of the action of selection in preserving or eliminating specific mutants. Genetics is thus the basic science for the study of evolutionary problems. Study of genetics at a more advanced and technical level than here presented must also include factual details of the types just listed.

Mutation of the chromosome set

In the beginning of our study of mutation we noted that mutational changes may affect a single gene or locus but can also alter whole chromosomes. Among the many groups of facts hinted at in this statement, some of them rather complicated, only two will be described because of their practical importance, as well as their relation to evolution. The first is mutation by doubling of the entire chromosome set, an event not uncommon in plants but rare in animals. An example, which started investigation of this field when it was first recognized, was the sudden appearance, as a mutant, of a giant evening primrose (pictured in Fig. 42). It was discovered that this, as well as many similar giant forms among plants, originated from a doubling of the chromosome number, which, in many cases, entails doubling of cell size and in consequence of total plant size. Such a plant has 4 of each kind of chromosome rather than 2. Nowadays a very effective method is known for inducing the chromosomes to double in this way, namely, treatment of the seeds with the drug colchicine. This obviously supplies the plant breeder who wants larger leaves or flowers with a new tool, and it is widely so used.

The second group of facts can be described as "mutation" only by somewhat stretching the meaning of the term. It is a type of hereditary change in a single step which is frequent in plants,

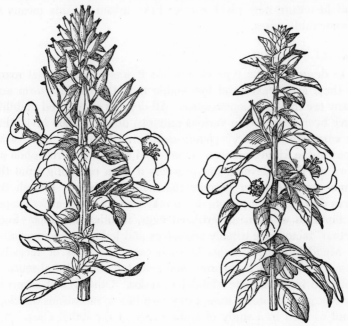

FIG. 42. The evening primrose *Oenothera lamarckiana* (*right*) and its giant mutant (*gigas*) by doubling of the chromosome set.

though almost unknown in animals. Indeed, many plant species have originated by this process. When 2 plant species are crossed, it sometimes happens that the chromosomes from the mother and father are so different, so incompatible, that they fail to pair or synapse properly before the maturation divisions of the hybrid gametes. Abnormal gametes are thus formed which contain 1 set of chromosomes from each parent species. If such gametes are produced by both male and female flower elements and fertilization occurs between them, the product is an organism with 4 sets of chromosomes, 2 from each parental species. When this type forms gametes there is no longer any difficulty in

141

normal pairing, for the 2 sets from each parental species pair among themselves in the usual way. This hybrid "mutant" can therefore breed true. The classic example of this situation is the origin of our tobacco plants from 2 wild species and a cross between horseradish and cabbage, resulting in a new constant type. Many of our cultivated plants originated in this fashion; and in nature new plant species have arisen by this means in innumerable cases.

Lethal mutation

In describing the type of mutants it was observed that many of them are weaker and less viable than the original form and many are freakish monstrosities. All degrees of reduced viability have been observed in various mutants, down to 100% inviability or complete "lethality" (*letalis*-deadly). There are also variations in the killing process. One lethal mutant in Drosophila allows the fly to develop but prevents it from emerging from the pupa case. Another permits the maggot to grow, though the larva dies before pupation; death may also occur at earlier stages, in embryos or even in fertilized eggs, in other mutants. Such "lethal" factors are usually recessives and lethal as homozygotes; in Mendelian experiments in such cases the class of recessive homozygotes will be missing and unobtainable. Its absence is reflected in incomplete Mendelian ratios. Otherwise it seems to have no visible effects, except those leading to monstrous development as seen in a study of embryology of the lethal class. Another type of lethal gene is remarkable in that the gene has a viable mutant effect appearing in the heterozygote, though the homozygous dominant is lethal. The best-known example is yellow fur in mice; the gene that produces the yellow coat color acts also as a recessive lethal. Yellow mice are therefore always heterozygous; when 2 yellows are mated they produce ⅓ not yellow, ⅔ yellow (ratio 1 : 2), the homozygous yellows being absent. The latter, however, can be found dying at an early developmental stage in the womb of the mother. Also noteworthy is the fact that many dominant mutants are lethal when homozygous, a phenomenon not yet clearly understood. Some factors of this kind have been important in animal husbandry, geneticists having discovered that stillborn abnormal calves were the result of the presence of such a lethal mutant, which

142

could be bred out of the stock once it had been identified. Such mutants are known in man. Among them, the dominant mutant that produces fingers lacking one joint, as mentioned in another chapter, is responsible, when homozygous, for stillborn monstrosities.

These last discussions require that we return once more to the subject of experimentally produced mutations. The most powerful agent for the production of mutations is the radiations which the physicist calls ionizing radiations. Foremost among these are the X-rays that cause mutations, increasing in number in proportion to the increase of the dosage of rays (usually measured in Roentgen units [r]). In the last decades the use of X-rays for purposes of medical diagnosis and treatment has increased immensely. Since the doses employed may well reach the amount needed for induction of a perceptible mutation rate it is important that precautions are taken with people still liable to beget children, so as to prevent irradiation of their sex glands with dangerous doses. As lethal mutants are so frequent among the induced mutants and, in addition, other mutants tend to produce abnormalities, even a small induced mutation rate may result in sorrow for those affected. Though there is no reason to become hysterical on this subject, it is wise to take the necessary precautions to protect the sex glands.

The same problem has become still more acute in the so-called atomic age, for atomic fission results in the release of immensely powerful radiations that are expected (and actually known) to produce large numbers of lethal and deleterious mutants. Therefore, all people of reproductive age working in atomic plants must be carefully screened from damaging radiations. If ever the horror of the atomic bomb should recur, the consequences for the descendants of the survivors are equally horrid to contemplate.

Sex Chromosomes
and Sex-Linked Inheritance

The picture of the chromosome set of Drosophila seen earlier (Fig. 33) revealed a peculiarity not discussed at the time: a difference between the female and male chromosome sets. On other occasions, too, we have encountered but thrust aside facts which indicated that sex is somehow connected with heredity. We are now ready to consider this important relation.

The cycle of the sex chromosomes

We have seen that the chromosome number is constant in the cells of each species. Further, we have established that the mature gametes contain only half the number, the reduced number of chromosomes, including 1 of each type of chromosome. At fertilization the maternal and paternal set are brought together and the normal number of chromosomes is restored, 2 sets of identical chromosomes, a pair of each kind. The chromosome number, therefore, must be an even one after fertilization. In view of these reasonable expectations, it was rather a shock to investigators to find in studying the sex cells of certain bugs and grasshoppers an odd number of chromosomes; when the individual pairs were accounted for, 1 chromosome was left without a partner. After some detours and misinterpretations it was discovered that this odd chromosome, called the X-chromosome because of its originally unknown function, has to do with the determination of sex or, more correctly, the mechanism which ensures that, as a rule, equal numbers of males and females result from fertilization.

144

Let us first seek to understand the elementary facts, studying one of the classical examples, a bug. In Fig. 43 its chromosomal

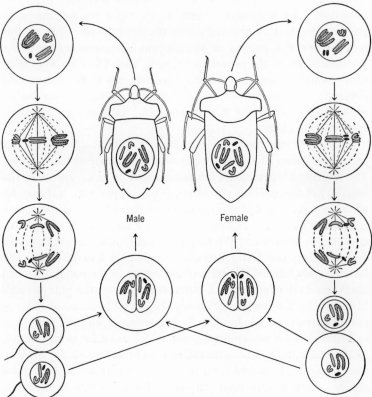

Fig. 43. A diagram of the cycle of the sex chromosomes in a bug. In the center, female and male with a typical nucleus drawn into them; 4 pairs of chromosomes, the small black ones being the sex chromosomes. On the left, the maturation division of the sperm cells resulting in 2 types of sperm, with and without sex chromosome (the second maturation division is left out to simplify matters). On the right, the maturation division of the egg (again only 1) resulting in eggs all of which contain the sex chromosome. Below, the 2 types of fertilization producing the 2 sexes.

cycle is illustrated. As on previous occasions the correct number of chromosomes is not represented because their large number (22 and more) would obscure the figures; instead, a normal number of 8 chromosomes is assumed, distinguishable as 4 pairs, 1 pair large and horseshoe-shaped, 1 pair small and horseshoe-

145

shaped, 1 pair rodlike, and 1 pair dotlike. In the center are a male and a female, each with a nucleus inside showing the typical chromosome set. The female has the normal set, the 4 pairs just described. By following arrows to the right we see the well-known processes of the reduction divisions in the eggs of this female: first the pairing of homologous chromosomes, next the division figure of the reduction division, then the reduction division (as before, and for the same reasons, we ignore the second division), and finally the mature egg cell (with a polar body) containing 1 set of the 4 chromosomes. Of course, all mature eggs will be alike.

On the left side the male is drawn. We see at once that it has the odd number of chromosomes which introduced this subject. The 3 larger chromosomes are represented as pairs, just as in the female, but the smallest chromosome has no partner. (It may be added at once that it is of no importance that the odd chromosome is here the smallest. In another species it might be the largest or anything in between.) We see, thus, that females and males have different chromosome numbers, 8 in the female, 7 in the male. We have already labeled the extra chromosome in the male, the small black one in the figure, the X-chromosome; since the pair of small black ones in the female are clearly the same chromosome it is apparent that the female has two X-chromosomes, and the male one, in addition to the remaining 3 pairs, which are alike in both sexes. The X-chromosomes are also called sex chromosomes, for obvious reasons, and a technical term for the other chromosomes is *autosomes*. Now we are ready to follow the formation of the male gametes, following arrows to the left. The first cell shows the pairing of chromosomes in the male sex cells prior to the reduction division. The 3 pairs of autosomes pair exactly as in the female cells. But the X-chromosome has no partner and therefore remains single. The next cell shows the arrangement for the reduction division, in which—as the following cell shows—the autosomes are separated exactly as in the female. The X-chromosome, however, having no partner, is pulled to only 1 pole. After completion of division, therefore, 2 types of sperm cells are formed, those with and those without the X-chromosome. The 2 types of sperm are produced in equal numbers; so, calling the autosomes A, we can say that the sperms formed are one-half $3A$, the other half $3A + X$.

146

There is, we see, only 1 type of egg—with the constitution $3A + X$—available for fertilization, along with 2 types of sperm; in fertilization we must then obtain equal numbers of the unions: eggs $(3A + X)$ with sperm $(3A + X)$, i.e., $6A + 2X$; and $(3A + X)$ with $3A$, i.e., $6A + X$ (see arrows in figure). In other words, half the offspring will have two X's, half only one, in addition to the 3 pairs of autosomes. But these were the actual chromosome numbers for the two sexes. The X-chromosome mechanism thus takes care of the production of the two sexes in equal proportions; the X-chromosome of the sperm cell, in this case, is female-determining, its absence having a male-determining effect (photos of X-chromosomes in ♀ and ♂ Fig. 17C).

This astonishing fact has since been proved to be of general occurrence. An X-chromosome mechanism for sex determination has been found in all animals with two sexes—mammals, including man, birds and reptiles, insects of any description, and many still lower animals—as well as for plants with separate sexes. However, just as the details of chromosome structure, size, shape, and number vary in different groups of organisms, so the details of behavior of the sex chromosomes exhibit a number of variations. One, the relative size of the sex chromosomes, has already been mentioned; there are also some more important variations.

One important variation is actually more common than the simple type described, although the decisive element, that $2X =$ one sex and $1X =$ the other sex, is completely unchanged. This is the situation already illustrated for Drosophila (Fig. 33). If we merely count the chromosomes, we find that both sexes have the same number. But upon examining the pairs closely we find (Fig. 33) that 1 of the pairs consists of identical partners in the female but of entirely dissimilar chromosomes in the male. In the Drosophila female there are 2 pairs of long chromosomes, 1 pair of dotlike chromosomes, and 1 pair of rods. In the male cell, however, although the long chromosomes and the dots are like those in the female, there is only a single rod, which has a partner shaped like a hook. Clearly, the long chromosomes and dots are the 3 pairs of autosomes, whereas the rods are the X-chromosomes, 2 in the female and 1 in the male. But the male X has a partner, the hook; this we call the Y-chromosome. It is obvious that the entire process of sex determination is exactly the same as in the

147

first example: $2X = ♀$, $1X = ♂$. In the male-determining sperm cell the lack of an X means also the presence of a Y,

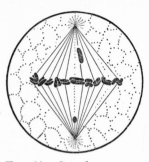

which is thus handed down only from father to son and normally never enters a female. Accordingly, the Y chromosome does not seem to be essential for sex determination and might just as well be absent. Why it is so frequently found is a problem that cannot be discussed without more genetical knowledge than is presented within the limits of this introduction. As was the case with the X-chromosome, the Y may be large or small, different in shape from the X or not (it may even be indistinguishable from the X under the microscope, but proper genetical analysis will find it out). Man has very large X-chromosomes and a small Y (Fig. 44) which, at pairing before reduction division, appears almost like a small knob at the tip of the X.

Fig. 44. Sex chromosomes in the maturation division of man; the large X and the short Y going to the poles ahead of the autosomes (not all autosomes drawn).

Types of the sex chromosome mechanism

A much more important variation of the X-chromosome mechanism exists. In our examples thus far—the bug, Drosphila, and man—the female has had 2 sex chromosomes, the male only 1. This is, in fact, the most common situation, found in mammals, frogs, beetles, grasshoppers, and many other groups of animals, as well as in most plants with separate sexes. But it is not everywhere present. A number of classes of animals and plants have exactly the opposite condition, namely, 1 sex chromosome in the female, 2 in the male. This is typical for birds and reptiles, for salamanders and newts, for butterflies and moths, and for strawberries. The only real difference this makes in the sex-determining mechanism is that in these cases 2 types of eggs and only 1 of sperm are produced. Everything is thus exactly as in the preceding description, except that now we must speak of "female" where we previously said "male," and vice versa. It is very difficult to formulate an opinion as to how and why these 2 types of sex-determining mechanisms originated, but there is

148

certainly a historical element in their distribution. The closely related birds and reptiles have the same type of mechanism; fishes, which are the lowest vertebrates and near the roots of the evolutionary tree of the whole group, have both types even today. We cannot enter here upon a detailed discussion but must rest content to know the facts, whatever their biological history.

I said that the X-chromosomes control sex determination. This statement is correct so far as it goes, but not complete. If this were the exact situation, a fly with two X-chromosomes should always be a female and one with a single X a male. This is certainly the usual case. But it is not invariable. Indeed, genetic conditions can be produced experimentally in which a $2X$ fly develops into a male and a $1X$ fly into a female. In a moth, where the female has normally only one X, the male two, a $1X$ individual may become a male or any stage between a fully formed female and a complete male—i.e., a so-called intersex—and, correspondingly, a $2X$ individual may become a female or an intersex. These aberrations show that the X-chromosomes constitute a device for distributing something within them, something needed for sex determination, in single or double quantities. If the content of the X-chromosome, its genetic factors, is changed experimentally, the normal result of the mechanism may be overridden in whole (giving sex reversal) or in part (giving intersexuality). Sex determination, though it is accomplished by the $2X$-$1X$ machinery, is thus fundamentally a genetic problem, relating to the sex-determining factors carried in the chromosomes. These facts, however, are too complicated for detailed presentation at an introductory level.

Control of the chromosomal mechanism of sex determination

Another problem is posed by the phenomenon of sex determination, namely, experimental control of the sex of offspring. By this I do not refer to the possibility of sex reversal in an individual under the experimental manipulations at which I have just hinted. What is meant is control of the normal $1X$-$2X$ mechanism to produce at will females alone, males alone, or some ratio between them other than the normal equality. If, for example, we could prevent every sperm cell with an X-chromosome from entering into fertilization, we could (in $1X$ = male forms) restrict ourselves to male progeny alone. Possible methods of which one may think might depend upon different rates of movement of X- as opposed to Y-sperms, or differential susceptibility to poisons, or making eggs impenetrable to one type of sperm. To date, no one has succeeded in thus controlling fertilization in man or domestic animals. The only positive results yet obtained relate to a moth, in which high temperature modified the reduction division of the egg so that most or all eggs were Y-eggs, destined to become males; this is at least a first step in demonstrating the feasibility of influencing the sex-determining mechanism.

Though the geneticist is, thus far, almost unable to force the mechanism of the sex chromosomes to follow a desired pattern, nature can do so in certain cases. One of these may be discussed. In a considerable number of animals the life cycle does not involve simply the production of one identical generation after another; their life stories are more complicated, probably as adaptations to very special conditions of life. In some instances this special life cycle is linked to special features of sexual reproduction. Good examples are the plant lice, the aphids, and especially a rather pernicious pest of grapevines. The egg of this latter form (Phylloxera), after hibernating in the soil, hatches in the spring. Every single individual emerging is a female. Something must therefore have interfered with the production of males. The females are able to reproduce without the aid of males; their eggs can develop without being fertilized. This is called "virginal reproduction" or *parthenogenesis* (*parthenos* = virgin). From these parthenogenetic eggs only females hatch out; they, in their turn, produce parthenogenetic daughters. This may go on all through the summer until, in late summer, a batch of parthenogenetic eggs suddenly yields both sexes, males and females. These males fertilize the females, and the fertilized eggs overwinter. They are the eggs from which we started tracing the cycle, and all of them develop into females. How is all this possible within the framework of the sex chromosome mechanism? In this case the mechanism is under the control of the sex cells, as will become apparent when we follow the chromosomes through the generations (see Fig. 45).

150

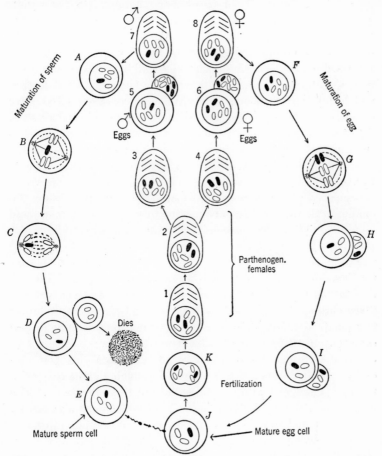

Fig. 45. The cycle of the sex chromosomes in the aphid of the grapevine. In the center below (1) the stem mother, with the chromosomes of her cells, producing parthenogenetically 2 generations of females (2, 3, 4). Number 4 produces another generation of females parthenogenetically (no reduction of chromosomes in the eggs [No. 6]). The female (No. 3) produces males (No. 7) by discarding 1 sex chromosome during the formation of a polar body (No. 5). The left outer circle shows maturation of the sperm of the male (No. 7) in 5 stages, A–E. In C and D, the reduction division, sperm cells, with and without X, are produced. The smaller one, without X, degenerates (E) and only sperm with X can fertilize. The outer circle on the right presents the maturation division of the egg (F–J). All eggs contain X. K is the fertilization, and out of the fertilized egg the stem mother (No. 1) will hatch.

151

We shall start with the first female hatching in the spring, coming from a fertilized egg; this is the so-called stem mother (No. 1, below center of picture). In this species the normal chromosome number is 6, i.e., 3 pairs, of which 1 pair in the female are the X-chromosomes (marked black, whereas the 2 pairs of autosomes are shown in white). The eggs of this female, which develop parthenogenetically, do not undergo a reduction division and therefore develop with the normal number of chromosomes. The daughters thus have exactly the same chromosome complement as the mother, including the two X-chromosomes which make for femaleness (parthenogenetic female in Fig. 45(2), following arrow). The same situation occurs in the succeeding parthenogenetic generations, which are not included in the figure. Then comes the time when both males and females are produced parthenogenetically. The eggs of 2 females (Nos. 3, 4) are pictured, 1 producing females (No. 4), 1 giving rise to males (No. 3). On the right (female egg, No. 6) we see the female-producing egg with a polar body, without reduction division, just as in the preceding generations. The egg still has 2 sex chromosomes. To the left is pictured the male-producing egg (male egg, No. 5), which also does not undergo a reduction division. But when the division figure forms and one split half of both X-chromosomes should go to each pole—this being an ordinary cell division—one daughter X which should remain in the egg "changes its mind" and goes into the polar body. The egg is left with only 5 chromosomes, 1 of which is an X; since 1X determines maleness in this species as in our other examples, this egg develops into a male (No. 7, top of the central group). Here, then, some unknown force at the time of formation of one polar body by ordinary cell division threw 1 chromosome out of the egg and thus made the egg male-determined.

The circle on the right starting with the last female (No. 8) shows what happens in her eggs. This female is no longer parthenogenetic. An unknown condition causes her egg to undergo normal reduction divisions, the prerequisite for fertilization, and a mature egg results (shown by stages F to I) which has 1 set of 3 chromosomes. On the left we see the maturation of the sperm cells produced by the male with 5 chromosomes (A–E). According to all we know, 2 types of sperm cells should be formed in equal numbers, 1 with and 1 without an X. This

152

is exactly what happens (C, D). But again an unknown condition of force interferes and makes the reduction division an unequal one for the cytoplasm; the female-determining gamete, the cell receiving the X, also receives most of the cell substance, whereas the other cell, lacking the X, remains a small, seemingly rudimentary bud (D). In fact, this latter cell cannot transform into a mature sperm because all the ingredients for this transformation have gone into the larger cell. The rudimentary cell dies, and only female-determining sperm remains (E). The overwintering fertilized egg is therefore always female.

Sex-linked inheritance

The X-chromosomes thus control sex in the way alluded to above. They must contain sex-determining factors that produce a different effect when present in one vs. two quantities (= factors in one or two X-chromosomes); we shall not discuss the details of this action here. Moreover, in view of the fact that X-chromosomes are frequently rather large and of the knowledge that chromosomes contain many genes, we may expect the X-chromosomes to contain genes of the same sort as those present in the autosomes, in addition to the specific sex determiners just discussed. This is, indeed, the case, and genes in the X-chromosome are of the same types and variety as those in other chromosomes. But can the hereditary transmission of these genes be the same as that of ordinary Mendelizing genes? Mendelian segregation, we have learned, is the consequence of the pairing of homologous chromosomes and their separation in the reduction divisions. Regardless of whether the gametes of a hybrid were produced in a male or in a female (ignoring some features of crossing over), we always found that 2 types of gametes were formed in equal numbers for 1 pair of alleles, located in 1 pair of chromosomes. This certainly cannot be true for alleles located in an X-chromosome. In the female, the $2X$ sex in most cases, a pair of alleles located in the pair of sex chromosomes will behave exactly as in any other case of Mendelian inheritance. The male sex, in contrast, cannot have a pair of alleles located in this chromosome; it has but a single gene of each in the X. The transmission of genes located in the X-chromosomes and the corresponding traits must therefore be different from that of ordinary genes, "ordinary" now meaning "located in the auto-

153

somes." We call a gene, as well as the trait controlled by it, that is located in an X-chromosome "sex-linked," and we speak of the sex-linked inheritance of such genes or characters.

In order to derive the specific features of sex-linked inheritance we must understand the following facts: If the mother has two X-chromosomes and the father only one, all sons will receive their sole X-chromosome from the mother, because the male-producing sperm does not have an X (i.e., it has a Y or nothing). For this reason a sex-linked gene cannot be transmitted directly from father to son but goes directly from the mother to her sons. A daughter is produced by the union of an egg with X and a sperm with X; a daughter, consequently, can receive a sex-linked gene directly from either parent. The following diagram illustrates this:

As may be expected, sex-linked inheritance has been found in a great many organisms in which sex chromosomes are also known. Man was actually the first organism in which sex-linked inheritance was observed, long before the rise of genetics afforded an explanation. The genetic interpretation was first discovered from a sex-linked character in a moth. Full insight into the principle that characters following the sex-linked scheme of inheritance are always based upon genes located in the X-chromosome was possible after numerous such mutant genes were discovered in Drosophila. Turning back to Fig. 39 showing the chromosome map of Drosophila, we may note that the chromosome called the first is actually the X-chromosome and many more mutant loci than are there entered on the map are known.

To see clearly how sex-linked inheritance works we shall return to the pedigree of bleeder's disease (Fig. 1) which started us on our genetic studies; this idealized pedigree is repeated as Fig. 46. When we first encountered this pedigree, the appearance of bleeders in the 4 generations seemed so irregular as to defy explanation. Some features became intelligible after we

154

had studied the inheritance of recessive Mendelizing genes. The final difficulty, namely, the absence of transmission of the disease from father to son but the occurrence of transmission to grandsons through a normal daughter, now becomes clear: Bleeder's disease is controlled by a sex-linked gene. Many similar pedigrees could be presented for a sizable array of human abnormalities and diseases. We can elucidate the mode of inheritance by following another well-known sex-linked trait in man, color

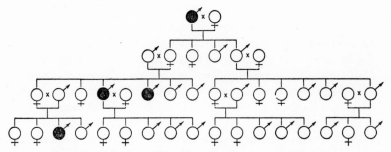

Fig. 46.   Pedigree of bleeder's disease, the same as Fig. 1.

blindness.[1] This defect in vision is rather rare in women but frequent in men. The reason is obvious. The defect is based upon a sex-linked recessive; since every man has only one X-chromosome, the recessive trait will be expressed if an X-chromosome carrying the gene is present; in other words, a man cannot simultaneously have a sex-linked recessive and its dominant allele. Women, having two X-chromosomes, may be heterozygous, but such heterozygotes will have normal vision; only those homozygous for the recessive sex-linked gene will be color blind. As we saw in an earlier chapter, human matings involving recessives for abnormality are most commonly in the nature of a backcross of a heterozygote to a homozygous dominant. Homozygous recessives thus have a small chance of occurring except after consanguineous matings. This is also true, in principle, for sex-linked characters. Color blindness, however, is sufficiently frequent to make the marriage of a heterozygous woman with a color-blind man not too rare a possibility.

[1] A number of different kinds of color blindness are known, which are genetically controlled. We simplify matters by studying only one, the most frequent type.

In detail, sex-linked inheritance will run as follows: Children of a normal (homozygous) woman and a color-blind father will all be normal; the sons receive their only X-chromosome from the normal mother, with her 2 "normal" X's, and are therefore free of color blindness and unable to transmit it. The daughters receive 1X from the normal mother, the other from the color-blind father, and are therefore heterozygous for that gene. They have normal sight but are transmitters of color blindness. Such a heterozygous woman, irrespective of her mate, will pass on to half her sons the X-chromosome carrying the gene for color blindness, whereas the other sons receive the normal allele. Now suppose that the heterozygous woman marries a color-blind man. Again half of her sons will be normal, the other half color blind. Half of her daughters receive the "normal X" from the mother and the "color-blind X" from the father; they are heterozygous normals like their mother. The other half of the daughters receive their mother's "color-blind X," as well as another "color-blind X" from the father. Result: homozygous color-blind daughters. And, now, what will the offspring of such a woman, homozygous for a sex-linked recessive, be when she marries a normal man? All her eggs contain the "color-blind X"; consequently, all her sons will be color blind. But since all of her daughters receive 1X, a "normal X," from their father, they all will be phenotypically normal heterozygous carriers. The daughters, thus are not color blind, like the father, whereas the sons are color blind like the mother. This so-called "crisscross" inheritance is obviously possible only for sex-linked characters.

Inheritance in the Y-chromosome

Let us return again to the map of the chromosomes of Drosophila (Fig. 39), where the first chromosome is the X-chromosome. We can now recall our study of crossing over, which supplied the basis for this map. Further, we recall the specific feature of crossing over in Drosophila, namely, that it occurs only in the formation of female gametes. In a pair of homologous autosomes (here chromosomes 2–4) crossing over could theoretically occur equally well in the male, and it is rather surprising that it does not do so. The X-chromosome, however, is always single in the male and, at least where a Y-chromosome is absent, crossing over involving the X cannot take place in male sex cells of any organism in which the male has but 1X. (In forms like birds, where the female has the 1X, the same is true, of course, for the eggs.) Sex-linked genes, we see, always behave, in regard to crossing over, like all Drosophila genes: Crossing over occurs only in one sex, that with the 2X's, even when the autosomes exhibit crossing over in both sexes.

The foregoing facts clearly require that a Y-chromosome, if present, shall not undergo crossing over with the X-chromosome. We have thus far treated the Y-chromosome as something entirely different from the X and essentially negligible, just as though it were not there, as is frequently the case. The situation is actually not quite so simple. Some Y-chromosomes do contain alleles of some genes in the X-chromosomes. This might be explained by assuming that the Y consists of 2 parts, 1 part being Y-substance proper (whatever that is) and another smaller or larger section being homologous to a portion of the X but lacking any sex-determining factors. We can symbolize such a structure in this way, the X being above the line and the Y below:

$$\frac{ABCDEF \quad \text{Sex } X}{ABC \quad Y\text{-substance}}$$

ABC are the genes in the Y allelic to genes in the X. Now let us suppose that A in the Y has mutated to a. How is this inherited? It is evident that a can be transmitted in the male line only, from father to son, to grandson, etc. Such cases are known, and a few diseases and abnormalities in man are inherited in this fashion, showing that the gene involved in each is located in the Y-chromosome. If the part ABC of the Y is homologous to the same section of the X, there is no reason why crossing over should not occur in that region. Thus it may be possible for a sex-linked trait, if located in that segment which has a homologue in the Y, to change its type of inheritance by crossing over into the special part of the Y. This, too, has actually been observed to happen. But we must stop here before we encounter the rather technical details.

A note on different genes with similar action

At this point we are ready to consider a fact which may look like nothing more than an illustration of the difficulties encountered in the study of human inheritance but which is really one of the important and basic facts of genetics. One determines the presence of a gene when a mutant is found which is demonstrated, by producing simple Mendelian segregation in crosses, to be allelic to the original condition. But we may encounter mutant phenotypes that look exactly alike but turn out to be completely different to the geneticist, i.e., to be mutants of different genes, which produce similar or identical phenotypes. Let us suppose, to take an example in man, that a definite disease, well defined clinically and recognized by any physician as N N-osis, is the result of destruction of a certain group of cells. This destruction may be the direct effect of a circulatory defect that suffocates the cells, or a nervous defect, or a metabolic defect that prevents removal of poisonous waste products, which leads to degeneration. Thus it is possible that mutant gene a, which affects the blood vessels, gene b, which affects certain nerves, and gene c, which affects chemical metabolism, all produce the same phenotype, the disease known as N N-osis. Pedigrees of this hereditary disease are now studied; one investigator finds it to be a dominant disease, to another it seems to be recessive, and to a third it appears to be sex-linked. Evidently, what is N N-osis to the physician is, to the geneticist, 3 different conditions, produced by 3 different mutants, perhaps in 3 different chromosomes. The geneticist is well acquainted with this phenomenon. In man it is not yet possible to analyze such a case completely. But in Drosophila, for example, tests for allelism and the localization of the several genes in the chromosomes would quickly resolve the problem. The geneticist would then name the disease or mutant character not by its phenotype (for example, N N-osis) but according to its mutant locus. A number of mutant phenotypes of this type are known in Drosophila. For example, a small nick at the tip of the wings may be based upon a mutant in the third chromosome or upon one in the second or upon one in the first (actually, more than one locus in each chromosome); all receive different names according to the different genes involved, not one, based on the identical phenotype.

Collaboration of Genes

General relations of gene and character

Thus far we have been looking at the relation of genes and the characters controlled by them in what one can call a naïve way, assuming that the gene is the representative in the chromosome of the visible character. If we try to visualize the consequences of such an inheritance, we should see that it makes the living organism a mosaic of individual gene-controlled attributes, assembled in the manner of a jigsaw puzzle. Everyone must realize, however, that the organism is a whole, acting as a unit in which all parts are integrated and subject to the overall organization of the entire body. This insight makes the mosaic idea and the naïve description of the gene-character relation appear rather crude. In point of fact, geneticists entertain no such crude concept; they recognize, instead, that all chromosomes and genes must interact in order to produce all characters as the result of their harmonious interplay. The mutant gene—and we must remember that a gene is recognized only when it has mutated—controls no more than a differential step in the collaboration of the whole. The meaning of this statement can be made clear by an example. A mutant gene in the first chromosome of Drosophila produces white eyes; i.e., the wild-type red eye pigment is not formed. In this case the collaboration of many, or all, genes, through the typical reactions that they control, results in developmental processes leading to the formation of a typical insect eye which is ready, at a particular stage, to receive a deposition of pigment or to lay down such pigment. In the presence of the mutant gene this one process alone, the pigment deposition, is somehow blocked. The mutant gene for white eye thus acts as a differential in a long chain of gene-controlled developmental processes; at a given point in development it makes one link in the reaction chain impossible, in this instance, the process by which some substance is changed into the red pigment.

It follows that the control of development by chromosomes and genes must operate as a closely knit, interdependent process or processes. One may compare it to the weaving of a complicated pattern by an automatic machine, where exact timing and direction are required for the placing of the many colored threads. If one of the thousands of movements fails, the whole pattern may be ruined. In a similar way the absence of a chromosome, or sometimes of only a part of a chromosome, or in certain cases of even an infinitesimally small portion, can so disturb the orderly, strictly coordinated and rigorously timed processes of embryogeny (meaning the genesis of the embryo or the process of development) as to make development impossible or monstrous. Recall, for example, the lethal factors. All the genes, thus, work together through exactly balanced reactions in development. Many geneticists have accepted the label "balance of the genes" for this concept, though it is actually a balance of gene-controlled developmental processes and reactions which is involved. For our present study the salient point is that, rather than one gene controlling one character, we have an interplay of all gene-controlled processes leading to production of a definite character, which, however, may be altered by mutants of one or another gene disrupting one or another stage in the developmental processes.

Interactions of genes in producing the phenotype

1. The Combs of Fowl. Apart from these general aspects of the relation gene-character, a number of special cases have been studied which entail specific and much simpler interactions between genes. A few of the classic examples will be discussed. The first of these is the inheritance of comb shape in fowl. We shall consider only 4 types, all of which occur as the characteristic comb in different breeds of chicken (see Fig. 47). There is the typical single comb, the usual comb of barnyard fowl as well as of the wild jungle fowl, ancestor of our domestic breeds. Another comb type has a clump of red, warty masses at the base

160

attached to a more or less elongated, fleshy, finger-like process; this has been given the poetic name of rose comb. A third comb consists only of rows of thickenings which have been likened to peas and thus is known as the pea comb. The fourth type forms a spongelike mass on the bird's forehead and has been called the walnut comb. In a Mendelian cross between rose comb and single comb, F_1 is rose and F_2 segregates into 3 rose : 1 single

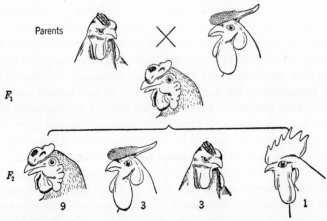

FIG. 47. Inheritance of some types of combs in fowl: (*first row*) pea comb crossed with rose comb; (*second row*) the hybrid with walnut comb; (*third row*) the F_2 segregation into 9 walnut, 3 rose, 3 pea, and 1 single comb.

comb. Since single comb is the ancestral type, rose comb must have arisen as a dominant mutation from single comb. A cross between pea comb and single comb gives similar results: In F_1 pea comb is dominant, and in F_2 segregation of 3 pea : 1 single occurs. Pea comb, too, originated as a dominant mutant from single. Now rose comb is crossed with pea comb. All F_1 chickens have a walnut comb. If we did not know of the existence of a walnut comb in certain breeds, we should say that a completely new and novel type had originated in this F_1. And the F_2 is still more remarkable. Segregation produces $\frac{9}{16}$ walnut comb, $\frac{3}{16}$ pea comb, $\frac{3}{16}$ rose comb, $\frac{1}{16}$ single comb. Not only have the parental and F_1 types segregated out, but, in addition, there has appeared another novelty—so far as this experiment is concerned—the ancestral single comb, which was not present in either parent of the cross (Fig. 47).

161

The F_2 ratio $9:3:3:1$ tells us immediately that 2 pairs of independent alleles located in different chromosomes are involved. The F_1 type tells us that in the double heterozygote walnut comb appears. We also know that both pea and rose comb are simple dominants. The 2 pairs of alleles in different chromosomes must therefore be dominant rose comb vs. no rose comb, and dominant pea comb vs. no pea comb. We have already noted that both rose and pea comb must be dominant mutants of the ancestral single comb. Accordingly, a homozygous rose comb, which is homozygous for the mutant in chromosome 1, must have the normal not-mutated gene in chromosome 2 (where a mutation of this gene would produce pea comb), thus being rose comb and not pea comb. Similarly, the pea-comb fowl, homozygous for a dominant gene in the second chromosome making pea comb, must have the normal, not-mutated gene in the first chromosome (for it, if mutated, would give rose comb), thus being pea comb, not rose comb. Thus, there is clearly a gene in both the first and second chromosomes which is involved in the formation of a comb. If neither has mutated, the single comb appears. If the gene in chromosome 1 mutates, alone, a rose comb is the result; if only the gene in chromosome 2 mutates, pea comb develops. Now let us write the results of this analysis in a Mendelian formula. If RR is homozygous rose comb and PP is homozygous pea comb, the crosses of each of these individually with single comb would be

P	$RR \times rr$	$PP \times pp$
F_1	Rr	Pp
F_2	$1\ RR : 2\ Rr : 1\ rr$	$1\ PP : 2\ Pp : 1\ pp$
	3 rose : 1 single	3 pea : 1 single

It is obvious that in both cases the recessive allele from which each dominant arose by mutation stands for single. The cross between pea and rose must therefore be symbolized as

$$RRpp \times rrPP$$

This means, as we have seen, that each individual has the normal alleles for single in the chromosome which has not mutated. The gametes of the rose fowl are Rp and those of the pea bird rP.

162

F_1 from this cross is therefore the double heterozygote $RrPp$. This F_1, we saw, had a walnut comb. Why should this be? Thinking out what may happen in this double heterozygote, we must first grasp the difference between this and our former example, black and short-haired F_1 guinea pigs. In the guinea pigs the 2 pairs of alleles affected different external characters, namely, color and length of hair. Both dominants could therefore appear simultaneously. In the present example, however, both dominants affect the same character, shape of comb. In such a situation we might anticipate that the rose-comb factor will act so strongly in development that the pea comb is completely obscured, or that the opposite will happen in favor of pea comb. Exactly this type of result does occur in some cases, one dominant taking complete and apparently exclusive effect despite the presence of another dominant affecting the same organ. One could call such a relation a kind of superdominance; it is actually called *epistasis* (= standing above), and we shall soon study examples. The third possibility is that the 2 dominants simultaneously influence the development of the organ, each in its own way; development will consequently be an addition of the 2 types of effect or some kind of compromise between the 2 developmental processes, one toward rose, the other toward pea comb. This compromise product has the final form we call walnut comb. Walnut comb can, of course, also exist in the homozygous state $PPRR$; it is always based upon the 2 dominants, whether we produce it by crossing pea and rose or find it true-breeding in some domestic breed.

Now we come to the F_2. The 16 combinations, easily derived in a Roman square, give the following genotypes:

1 *RRPP* 1 *RRpp* 1 *rrPP* 1 *rrpp*

2 *RrPP* 2 *Rrpp* 2 *rrPp*

2 *RRPp*

4 *RrPp*

i.e., 9 walnut 3 rose 3 pea 1 single

The presence of both dominants produces a walnut comb, R dominant alone a rose comb, P dominant alone a pea comb, and no dominants at all a single comb.

Let us further examine the $\frac{1}{16}$ class with single comb, produced by the absence of the dominant mutants that, in course of the history of domestication of fowl, changed the wild-type single comb into rose or pea comb. Two genes thus exist in different chromosomes which have to do with the production or, more correctly, the control of development leading to the single comb. Examination of various domestic breeds will reveal other comb shapes; these upon analysis turn out to be based upon simple Mendelian mutants of genes different from those studied in the present example. Thus it can be demonstrated that a considerable number of loci scattered along many or all of the chromosomes control the shape of a comb and each of them may mutate and thus change the comb shape in some way. Now suppose that only the single and pea combs were known and the conclusion asserted—the one we called naïve at the beginning of this chapter—that this gene is *the* gene for comb form. The foregoing discussion makes clear how erroneous such a conclusion would be. First we found one factor for comb shape, then a second, and afterwards, many. Where is the limit? There is, we answer, no limit to the number of genes actually involved, but only a limit to the number recognized because we have found them mutated. This very important conclusion gives us the reason we have so thoroughly examined our example: not that we are much concerned with the combs of chickens but because study of them could teach us a lesson applicable to the whole of Mendelian heredity.

2. Mendelism and Atavism. We may interrupt our analysis for a moment to emphasize another aspect of the present discussion, a problem already hinted at repeatedly. In the older literature on evolution, including Darwin's writings, a phenomenon called *atavism* (*atavus* = ancestor) is frequently discussed. Atavism refers to the appearance in a line of plants or animals of a variant, produced by mutation or segregation after crossing, which is precisely like the supposed ancestral form. This new type is said to be atavistic, a return to the known or hypothetical ancestral type. Darwin's famous example was the production, by crosses among various domestic breeds of very different type, color, and form, of pigeons identical in appearance to wild rock pigeons. In fact, Darwin considered this a proof of the previously suspected origin of domestic pigeons from the blue rock

164

pigeon. Mendelian inheritance, of course, was unknown to Darwin. In his day our example, in which the ancestral comb shape, that of the wild jungle fowl of Malaya, appeared in the F_2 of a cross between 2 different domestic breeds (rose and pea), would certainly have been regarded as atavistic. Now, however, we see clearly that atavism involves no mystical return to an ancestral type. It is, rather, the necessary and controllable outcome of the genic composition of the progenitors of the atavistic individual.

Another example of atavism will be presented because it reveals further facts on the interaction of Mendelizing genes. A famous cross first made in the early days of Mendelism (as was the comb cross) was one between 2 races of fowl, both with almost white plumage. All the F_1 progeny bore the brilliant many-colored plumage which is frequently seen in unimproved barnyard stock and is very like the plumage of the ancestral jungle fowl. Remembering the terminology of Drosophila mutants, we can call this varied plumage the wild type. In F_2 this type and the parental white segregated in the strange ratio of $\frac{9}{16}$ wild : $\frac{7}{16}$ white. From this outcome the reader may already guess that 2 pairs of alleles are involved and that the 2 white races serving as parents must be genetically different. In order to understand this result without requiring a detailed knowledge of the chemistry of pigment formation we need merely point out a general feature of the production of coloring material of the sort found in feathers, ignoring the fact that the structure of the feather also contributes to its colors. In general, a colorless substance is synthesized, and then it is transformed into a pigment by the action of an enzyme. If a dominant gene exists which is necessary for the elaboration of the precursor substance, and if another dominant gene is essential for production of the enzyme, a bird having only 1 of these dominants by itself will be non-colored or white, though all other genetic conditions for colored plumage may be satisfied. After the two white strains, one carrying the gene for formation of pigment precursor substance, the other having the gene for enzyme production, are crossed, both dominants come together and pigment appears. But, now, why does the entire color pattern of the wild fowl appear? The answer is supplied by our discussion of comb shape. Both of the white breeds were derived from a wild type

165

containing all the genes necessary for development of the characteristic, colorful plumage pattern. A mutation in one strain changed one of the genes necessary for pigment precursor production into an allele impeding synthesis of the substance; in the other strain a gene in a different chromosome needed for enzyme synthesis had mutated to an allele that blocks enzyme formation. Each strain was thus potentially wild type except for 1 mutant gene, the mutant being different in each strain.

Now that we understand the results, we can describe them in simple Mendelian symbolism, not mentioning all the genes involved in the development of the wild type (but taking these for granted), while tracing only the 2 differential mutant genes. We may call the pigment precursor gene C and its recessive allele c, the enzyme-producing gene E and its mutant allele e. In both breeds 1 gene is present as a mutant, the other as the wild-type dominant. Hence, the cross is $CCee \times ccEE$. The F_1 are $CcEc$; both dominants being present, they are colored. In F_2 the 16 combinations of the Roman square are produced; among these, we know, 9 contain both dominants, 3 have only 1 of the dominants, 3 have only the other dominant, and 1 is homozygous for both recessives. Since only the individuals having both dominants can be colored, the result is $\%_{16}$ colored : $\frac{7}{16}$ white.

3. The Hierarchy of Color Genes in Mice. To these two examples illustrating the mode of collaboration of genes and at the same time clarifying our ideas on the relation of gene to character we shall add a third, embodying certain variations on the general theme of this chapter and summarizing this whole body of facts. Again it is an example of color in animals, namely, fur color in mice. Fanciers delight in breeding color races of mice, rats, guinea pigs, and rabbits, the last-mentioned also serving commercial ends. Among tame mice there are many such breeds—black, white, cinnamon, chocolate, silver, selfs, piebalds, albinos. All these color variants have been analyzed genetically and the results give us a good idea of the collaboration of many pairs of alleles all affecting the same visible character, hair pigmentation. Let us begin with 2 mice, one the wild-type gray mouse necessarily bearing all the unmutated alleles, the other an albino. Albinism is a relatively common mutant in many different animals, among them amphibians, birds, and mammals, including

166

man. In these albinos a recessive mutant gene prevents the formation of any pigment in the skin, the hair, and even the eyes; the eyes are consequently red and extremely sensitive to light. An albino mouse crossed to the wild type produces normal grays in the F_1 and an F_2 of 3 gray : 1 albino, as expected of a simple recessive. But if we repeat the same experiment with another albino strain, we might be surprised at the result: an F_2 including blacks in addition to the grays and albinos. To be precise, we should count $9/16$ grays, $3/16$ blacks, and $4/16$ albinos. Obviously we have here segregation for 2 independent pairs of alleles, and the unexpected black must somehow have resided in the albino.

Now let us recall the example of white fowl producing colored birds after crossing, the reason being that one strain had the gene for pigment precursor and the other had the gene for the enzyme needed to transform the precursor into pigment. To avoid becoming entangled in the (not-very-simple) chemistry of the process, we may speak noncommittally of pigment precursor and realisator. If it be assumed that albinism is the result of non-functioning of the realisator effect because of a recessive mutation, the allele for albinism, it follows that, in the presence of the homozygous albino gene, an albino must appear regardless of what precursor is present. Then, if there be many genes producing different precursors—for gray, black, brown, yellow, etc. —an albino may be potentially a mouse of any known color, or a piebald, but one unable to realize its color because of the effects of the albino gene. But after crossing Mendelian recombination may produce in F_2 an individual in which the color genes of the original albino have been separated from the albino gene and therefore been enabled to express this color. If this interpretation is correct, appearance of black in the F_2 of our experiment indicated that the albino parent was a black in which the realisator gene had mutated to its recessive, the albino allele. One may also expect that in other, similar experiments we should obtain still other colors in the F_2; and, in fact, we can thus identify albino strains derived from every known color variety, in which there has occurred a mutation of the realisator gene to its recessive allele. The new color crops up in the F_2, first, because the albino contained the proper color genes and, second, because the colored parent introduced into the cross the dominant realisator gene (mutated in the albino) which, in F_2, can recombine with whatever color gene the albino parent brought in.

To understand the exact ratio of our cross—9 gray : 3 black : 4 albino—we must be cognizant of another factor. The gray mouse must have the gene for wild-type color as well as the realisator gene needed for any color. Wild-type color is actually the result of the presence of a yellow ring near the tip of an otherwise black-pigmented hair. Each gray mouse therefore must have the gene for black pigment in addition to the wild-type gene that regulates distribution of the pigment. Remember the earlier description of the phenomenon of *epistasis*, the suppression or, more correctly, overlapping of the action of one dominant by that of another. In this sense the gray gene is epistatic over the black gene, which is located in a different chromosome; gray is visible only when both are present. When the gray gene mutates to its recessive allele, the process producing the ringed wild-type hair pattern ceases and the black gene, also present, can now fully control the phenotype, giving us a black mouse. Thus both gray and black have the black dominant gene; the gray has, in addition, the dominant for wild type, whereas the black lacks this dominant, that is to say, has the recessive of the wild-type color gene.

Now we are ready to understand the Mendelian ratio found. We call the wild-type factor *A* (this is derived from the name agouti for the wild-type color, referring to the color of a South American rodent of this name). The factor for black in another chromosome is *B*, and the gene described as the color realisator is *C* and is in a third chromosome. A true-breeding gray mouse is therefore (as far as this experiment goes) *AABBCC*, a black mouse is *aaBBCC*, and an albino derived as a mutant from black is *aaBBcc*. Since both parents are homozygous for *B*, all the offspring must have *BB* and we may omit this factor from our Mendelian formulae. Our cross is thus reduced to $AACC \times aacc$, a cross involving 2 independent pairs of alleles, giving 16 combinations in F_2. We can read these from a Roman square; to make the phenotypes of the combinations instantly recognizable we shall add the homozygous gene for black, *BB*, present throughout, though it could also be omitted and merely kept in mind:

168

	EGGS	AC	Ac	aC	ac
		ABC	ABc	aBC	aBc
	AC	ABC	ABC	ABC	ABC
		gray	gray	gray	gray
		1	2	3	4
		ABC	ABc	aBC	aBc
	Ac	ABc	ABc	ABc	ABc
SPERM		gray	albino	gray	albino
		5	6	7	8
		ABC	ABc	aBC	aBc
	aC	aBC	aBC	aBC	aBC
		gray	gray	black	black
		9	10	11	12
		ABC	ABc	aBC	aBc
	ac	aBc	aBc	aBc	aBc
		gray	albino	black	albino
		13	14	15	16

Nine combinations have ABC homozygous or heterozygous and are gray; 3 have BC but only aa and are black; and 4 have only cc and are therefore albinos.

In this example we have met AABBCC grays and aaBBCC blacks. It is also possible to have the gray factor AA present but the black BB mutated to its recessive allele, bb, giving AAbbCC. This recessive bb would make the hair brown in the absence of the agouti factor, as in aabbCC; with the gray factor, i.e., AAbbCC, the mouse is said to be cinnamon-colored. We could extend our analysis to still other color varieties; we should find that a recessive gene exists, again in another chromosome, which when homozygous dilutes all colors, producing hues for which the fanciers have special names. If we call this diluting gene dd, it follows that a not-diluted-color mouse must have the dominant allele to dd, namely DD. Therefore, for completeness, we should have to write for the gray mouse AABBCCDD and for the black aaBBCCDD. Now we can introduce a piebald mutant into our crosses; this will uncover another recessive, ss, the spotting factor, needed to produce this type. Not-spotted crossed to spotted will give a normal, and the F_2 will segregate into 3 self-colored to 1 piebald. The dominant alleles SS must therefore be present in all not-piebald mice. Our gray mouse now becomes *AABBCCDDSS*; *AABBCCDDss* would be a gray piebald; *aaBBCCDDss* a black piebald. It is hardly necessary to continue this analysis as far as geneticists have been able to go. The decisive point should be sufficiently clear already: When we say that a gene controls a given character, we tacitly include all the other genes, known or unknown, which contribute a share to the end result, this being changed in a typical way when any of the genes mutates. Since genes become recognizable only when they mutate, there is no theoretical limit but only an empirical one to the number contributing something to any developmental process. Details of their effects depend upon interrelations such as we have already studied—dominance, epistasis, collaboration, compromise.

Summative or Multiple Factors

Introduction

The preceding chapter considered the mode of collaboration of different genes in the production of a character, as illustrated by some classical examples, though any of the most diversified characters of various organisms could have been used. The gene that was represented as the chromosomal basis of a visible character turned out to be one of many genetic conditions which in this complicated interplay has only, one might say, the last word. We now turn to a related but different mode of collaboration of genes, namely, the production of a character by a more or less large number of genes, each having the same type of effect so that the end result is the sum total of all these partial actions. Because these genes are summative in effect and are generally numerous, one speaks of multiple factors or genes. Obviously, traits of a quantitative kind, such as size, shape, and length and weight of parts, most readily lend themselves to this type of control. These are precisely the kinds of characters frequently distinguishing forms in nature and most important in practical breeding: rate of growth, amount of meat or fat, length of limbs or neck, weight of wool, length of ears, shape of body, amount of milk, size of ear in corn, fat or protein or starch content in grains, amount and strength of straw, stature of man, etc. Multiple genes are thus of major importance in fundamental as well as applied genetics.

If a character like body size is regulated by a number of genes, each contributing its share to control of growth, one can visualize a number of possibilities. Only a few genes may be involved, each having a major share in the end effect. Or there may be

171

a large or very large number of genes, each of which has only a small share in the effect produced by the summation of all the partial effects. Moreover, each of the pairs of alleles may exhibit the phenomenon of dominance, so that AA and Aa have the same effect and share in the result. Alternatively, the heterozygote may have an intermediate effect, that is to say, two A's have twice the effect of one A. Again, each gene may have approximately the same effect, the total being simply this effect times the number of genes; or the individual factors may differ in amount of effect, this one contributing a little more, that one a little less, so that the sum total is arrived at by the addition of the more or less different individual actions. In one such situation some of the genes have very large effects, the rest only small effects. As an extreme example, one gene may control almost the entire result, the others having only a very little share.

Genetic modifiers

This last possibility must be explored further, for it leads to a very interesting group of facts. When a visible character based upon a certain gene is studied, the phenotype is frequently found to be somewhat variable, even though external conditions are constant so that the influence of a variable environment is practically excluded. As an example, take one of the wing mutants of Drosophila, in which a piece near the tip of the wing is missing. If we take a homozygous strain of this mutant, breed it under absolutely identical conditions, then measure the wing defect in many individuals, we shall find a considerable variation, ranging from small to large nicking of the wing. In the first chapter, we recall, it was shown that such variation may be nonhereditary, conditioned by the environment, or it may be hereditary based upon genetic factors. We found there that it is not difficult to discriminate between these two alternatives. If the variation is the product of known or unknown environmental agents, the offspring of parents taken from either extreme expression of the varying character (extreme minus or extreme plus) will not be different from the parental group. It will exhibit moreover the same kind and degree of variation as the parental group, whatever the precise phenotypes of the individual parents may have been. If the variation was hereditary, offspring of the larger variants will be themselves large; of small

172

variants, small; in other words, selection for degree of character, here size, will be possible. Selection can, we saw, be continued, until all genetic factors have been selected and made, as we should now say, homozygous. Thereafter the selected type will breed true, and no further selection can be effective. In the present experiment on wing defect external conditions were carefully regulated, but complete control is practically impossible. Some environmentally caused variation will therefore still be present. Selection provides the crucial test. If we can change the type by selection toward larger or smaller wing defects over a number of generations, until a maximum or minimum is reached which is not shifted further by continued selective breeding, the variation must be based upon genes influencing the amount of wing defect caused by the basic wing-nicking mutant gene. Genes which thus regulate the quantity of effect produced by other genes are called *modifiers*.

Our experiment has established that the line of flies homozygous for the mutant causing the wing defect contained many modifiers, which, in turn, can be made homozygous by continued selection. The results of genetical study generally show that such an array of modifiers, many of them heterozygous, will always be encountered, whatever the character studied; breeding work, consequently, often involves making these modifiers for a plus or minus effect homozygous. There is clearly no essential difference between gene interaction, as studied in the preceding chapter, and action of modifiers, only a difference in the status of our knowledge. If we know that in mice gene A controls the deposition of pigment in rings, and B controls formation of black pigment, the interaction of A and B is demonstrated by the known types $AABB$ = gray, $aaBB$ = black, $aabb$ = brown. If, instead, A has no apparent individual effect but, in the presence of B, changes black into gray, we can label A a modifier for B.

Modifiers without any other visible effect can thus be made homozygous by long-continued selection and close inbreeding; any mutant or other genetic type can be regarded as completely homozygous only when all its modifiers are also homozygous. Serious errors in the interpretation of breeding results have arisen from neglect of this fact. The fundamental geneticist who wishes to analyze the effects of definite genes will therefore try to work with a strain completely homozygous for all modifiers.

Elements of multiple-factor inheritance

After this general discussion we are ready to return to the study of the genetic details and consequences in multiple-factor inheritance. We shall assume the simplest condition; namely, the character in question is conditioned by a series of multiple genes each making the same contribution to the total effect, and the heterozygote for each pair of alleles has an effect intermediate between those of the homozygous dominants and the recessives. Thus, if $AA = 20$ units, Aa is 10; expressed differently, each individual dominant gene contributes 10 units.

For an example we could use any quantitative character of animals or plants. Assume that we are concerned with the inheritance of size in a species of mammal with 2 distinct and true-breeding races which differ in size. One race has, we assume, an average head-to-tail length of 100 cm., the other a length of 40 cm. The size of the larger race is based, we further assume, upon 3 pairs of multiple factors; in a real experiment this number might be very much larger, but it is simpler to derive the results for a small number of factors. The observed difference between the two races is then as follows: Both owe their initial growth up to 40 cm. to a series of genes common to both; these genes may therefore be neglected here. The large race has, in addition, 3 pairs of growth genes, call them $AABBCC$, which collectively contribute an extra 60 cm. of growth $(40 + 60 = 100)$. According to our suppositions, each of these individual genes (i.e., 1 gene in 1 chromosome) controls 10 cm. of growth beyond the basic length of 40 cm. The total size of any individual is therefore $40 + n \times 10$, n being the number of individual growth genes. The small race is thus $aabbcc = 40 + 0$; the large race, $40 + 6 \times 10 = 100$. The combinations $AaBbCc$ or $AABbcc$ or $aaBbCC$ would measure $40 + 3 \times 10 = 70$ cm. The cross is

large race $\times$ small race

P $AABBCC \times aabbcc$

F_1 $AaBbCc$

The F_1 is evidently exactly intermediate between the parents or 70 cm. long. The F_2 from this will follow the simple trihybrid

174

segregation we studied above, provided that A, B, and C are located in different chromosomes, giving the 8 types of gametes ABC, ABc, AbC, aBC, Abc, aBc, abC, abc, and 64 F_2 combinations. These can be obtained from a Roman square; in each combination we can count the number of growth genes A, B, and C (as shown in the square below).

ABC	ABC	ABC	ABC	ABC	ABC	ABC	ABC
ABC	ABc	AbC	aBC	Abc	aBc	abC	abc
6	5	5	5	4	4	4	3
ABc	ABc	ABc	ABc	ABc	ABc	ABc	ABc
ABC	ABc	AbC	aBC	Abc	aBc	abC	abc
5	4	4	4	3	3	3	2
AbC	AbC	AbC	AbC	AbC	AbC	AbC	AbC
ABC	ABc	AbC	aBC	Abc	aBc	abC	abc
5	4	4	4	3	3	3	2
aBC	aBC	aBC	aBC	aBC	aBC	aBC	aBC
ABC	ABc	AbC	aBC	Abc	aBc	abC	abc
5	4	4	4	3	3	3	2
Abc	Abc	Abc	Abc	Abc	Abc	Abc	Abc
ABC	ABc	AbC	aBC	Abc	aBc	abC	abc
4	3	3	3	2	2	2	1
aBc	aBc	aBc	aBc	aBc	aBc	aBc	aBc
ABC	ABc	AbC	aBC	Abc	aBc	abC	abc
4	3	3	3	2	2	2	1
abC	abC	abC	abC	abC	abC	abC	abC
ABC	ABc	AbC	aBC	Abc	aBc	abC	abc
4	3	3	3	2	2	2	1
abc	abc	abc	abc	abc	abc	abc	abc
ABC	ABc	AbC	aBC	Abc	aBc	abC	abc
3	2	2	2	1	1	1	0

Arranging the data in an orderly fashion, we find among the 64 F_2 combinations

  1 with 6 growth factors; i.e., size 100 cm.
  6 with 5 growth factors; i.e., size 90
  15 with 4 growth factors; i.e., size 80

175

20 with 3 growth factors; i.e., size 70
15 with 2 growth factors; i.e., size 60
6 with 1 growth factor; i.e., size 50
1 with 0 growth factors; i.e., size 40

We can arrange this result the following way:

Number of growth genes	6	5	4	3	2	1	0
Size classes in centimeters	100	90	80	70	60	50	40
Number of individuals	1	6	15	20	15	6	1

What do these results mean? In the F_2 we have 7 different sizes of animals. But, remembering the contents of the first chapter, we should hardly expect so strict a difference between, and uniformity within, the 7 classes. The genetic size of each class is only an ideal, the mean or average size found among many individuals. Single individuals will deviate more or less from this mean under the influence of environmental factors acting upon their development, as seen in the example of size in beans. In a real experiment, therefore, the 7 classes will not be discrete; instead, they will be connected by individuals of transitional size. We should find a continuous series of sizes between 40 and 100 cm., provided that we breed sufficiently large numbers of individuals. Among these phenotypes no clear-cut Mendelian segregation is visible, though we have seen how it has really taken place. The reader can appreciate how such facts could be used as examples of non-Mendelian inheritance before they were truly understood.

Another important point emerges from the F_2 classification. The largest number of individuals (20 out of 64) appeared in the class of intermediate size (70 cm.); the smallest number, 1, occurred in the extreme classes of largest and smallest size. The numbers increased symmetrically from the lowest to the greatest, both in the smaller and larger classes (1, 6, 15, 20, 15, 6, 1). This symmetrical arrangement is clearly that described in the first chapter as the curve of variation. There we saw—we recall the pinball machine, Fig. 7—that this symmetrical distribution of phenotypes occurs when we measure a large number of genetically identical individuals, the reason being that small differences in the environment affect development and pull the resulting phenotype a little above or below the ideal effect produced by the genetical constitution. If pure chance is at work, extreme deviations will be the rarest occurrences, a balance between deviations in one or the other direction will be the most frequent event, and superiority of the pulls in one direction will be the less frequent the more extreme they are. Phenotypes thus fall into a symmtrical curve of variation. And now we find exactly the same symmetrical distribution of the phenotypes around a mean in a Mendelian experiment, where we know the individuals are genetically different, actually including 7 different genotypes. What a source of potential error, as we shall soon see!

The F_2 series can teach us another important fact. The largest number of individuals (20 out of 64) were found in the intermediate-sized class of 70 cm. and thus were of the same size as the F_1 intermediates. Our F_2 series shows that among the 64 individuals 50 will range in size between 60 and 80 cm. Now suppose that we had worked with animals which produce only a few young per parental pair. With only 25 F_2 specimens it is rather probable that all of them will fall into these intermediate-sized classes; one might then conclude that the F_2 looks just like the F_1 and that there has been no Mendelian segregation but a constant intermediate inheritance. In the early days of genetics this kind of error was actually made. How easily it may occur becomes still clearer if we visualize a genetic difference caused by 6 pairs of multiple factors. Again we start with 2 races having the average sizes, 40 cm. and 100 cm., but now we have 6 pairs of alleles $AABBCCDDEEFF$, so that each gene controls 5 cm. of growth over and above the basic 40 cm., giving a total of 100. In F_2 there is segregation for the 6 pairs of alleles; a Roman square with 4096 squares would be needed to accommodate the combinations. A count of the distribution of size classes in F_2 would give us the following result (arranged like the F_2 series on p. 176):

Number of growth genes	12	11	10	9	8	7	6
Size classes in centimeters	100	95	90	85	80	75	70
Number of individuals	1	12	66	220	495	792	924

Number of growth genes	5	4	3	2	1	0
Size classes in centimeters	65	60	55	50	45	40
Number of individuals	792	495	220	66	12	1

177

Examining this series in the same way as before we find 3498 of the 4096 F_2 individuals in the intermediate classes of 60–80 cm.; thus even a fairly large F_2 generation, with, say, 500 animals, would most probably fall completely within these intermediate classes. So it is that the larger the number of multiple factors, the less conspicuous is the F_2 segregation.

Proving the interpretation

There have been and, in certain places, still are non-geneticists who point to the result and say: This is a trick; if you introduce enough multiple genes, you can explain away any result that does not agree with the Mendelian concept. It must therefore be asked how the correctness of the multiple-factor explanation can and has been proved. Using the same experiment, we must first measure all the F_1 individuals, supposedly averaging 70 cm. Environmentally caused variation produces some variation about this mean, so that we may find in the F_1

Size in centimeters	66	67	68	69	70	71	72	73	74
Number of individuals	2	9	12	17	35	18	13	8	r

These numbers are not ideal numbers but the sort that might occur in an actual experiment. Next, in the F_2 with 6 pairs of multiple alleles, we may find only animals in the intermediate classes between 60 and 80 cm. The exact result might be

Size in centimeters	60	61	62	63	64	65	66
Individuals	2	7	11	27	48	96	112

Size in centimeters	67	68	69	70	71	72	73
Individuals	180	240	330	339	285	260	129

Size in centimeters	74	75	76	77	78	79	80
Individuals	101	88	43	31	18	4	1

We see at once that, although the original parental sizes of 40 and 100 cm. did not segregate out, or even sizes approaching these, the variation in F_2 is much wider than that in F_1. This greater variation in F_2 is in itself an indication that multiple factors are involved.

An actual proof can be obtained from the following facts: Still using the same example (6 pairs of multiple factors, each

178

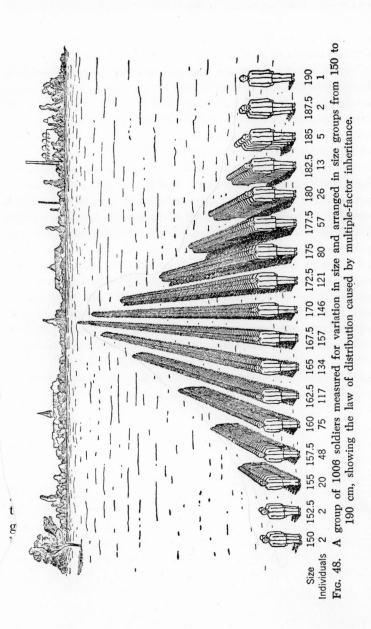

Size	150	152.5	155	157.5	160	162.5	165	167.5	170	172.5	175	177.5	180	182.5	185	187.5	190
Individuals	2	2	20	48	75	117	134	157	146	121	80	57	26	13	5	2	1

FIG. 48. A group of 1006 soldiers measured for variation in size and arranged in size groups from 150 to 190 cm, showing the law of distribution caused by multiple-factor inheritance.

commonly heterozygous. It seems that the number of growth genes involved in human stature is not very large; attempts have even been made to show that they individually affect the different increments of size, such as length of leg or rump.

While using man as an example, we may mention another instance of multiple factors in man for its general interest. Skin color, especially black and white, is the case in question, mentioned because completely mistaken ideas concerning it are common among laymen. The cross black $\times$ white produces children of intermediate color, or mulattoes. Popular belief is that mulattoes marrying among themselves will again produce mulattoes, for generation after generation. But the offspring of a mulatto and a white is a so-called quarter-blood or quadroon, and of a mulatto with a black a so-called three-quarter blood or sambo. When large numbers of children born from marriages between mulattoes are studied, it is quickly seen that their color is not at all uniform but varies widely from dark to light, exactly as expected if skin pigmentation is controlled by a series of multiple genes. One consequence is that pure whites and pure blacks, in regard to skin color, are expected to appear among segregants where large numbers are studied; further, selection by preferential mating of lighter segregants will favor the reappearance of white. Exact studies of mixed populations have supported these expectations; it is claimed that only 2 pairs of major factors are involved, plus what we have called modifiers.

Multiple Alleles

The basic facts

Up to this point our analysis of the facts of Mendelian inheritance has dealt with pairs of genes each located at a definite locus on a pair of homologous chromosomes. Such a locus or gene, we have seen, can change by mutation into a mutant gene, thus giving us a pair of alleles; it is the mutant gene, as repeatedly asserted, the difference from the normal condition, which permits recognition of the normal gene from which the mutant gene is derived. The facts studied thus far considered only a single mutant allele for each gene: The factor for black hair in guinea pigs mutated into one for white hair; the gene for normal wings in Drosophila, into one for vestigial wings; the locus of the production of the red eye, into one controlling white eye, etc. Expressed in symbols, A mutated to a, B to b, C to c, D to d, etc. Since a mutant very frequently has seemed to be a failure of production of the normal condition, early Mendelians thought that the recessive gene might really be the absence of its normal partner: White would be not black, long hair, absence of control of hair growth, etc. But since those early days it has been found that a given gene can mutate not merely to a single mutant condition but often to more than one and, in fact, many. The gene $+^w$ for red eyes in Drosophila (we remember this method of symbolizing the normal gene; see p. 115) can mutate into the allele w producing white eyes, and also into the alleles w^a for apricot eye, wch for cherry color, w^e for eosin eyes, and many more. Thus there is not a single allele to the original gene but many, giving *multiple alleles,* each the result of a mutation. *Multiple allelism* is the technical term applied to the phenomenon

185

of occurrence of multiple alleles. It is regrettable that the words *multiple alleles* sound so much like the multiple factors we have just studied, which are completely different things. Attempts have been made to overcome the confusion by calling the multiple factors—i.e., many genes of identical action each contributing a share in the production of a quantitative character—polymeric factors or summative factors or polygenes. But the old name multiple factors still sticks, and a warning against confusion with multiple alleles is therefore needed.

Multiple alleles are by no means a rare occurrence. As a matter of fact, all adequately studied genes in any organism whatsoever have been found to produce multiple alleles. Nor is there any rule as to how many alleles may arise at a locus. In some cases as many as 20 alleles of 1 gene have been discovered.

Characteristics

Now let us consider a few of the characteristics of multiple alleles. As may be expected, the members of a series of multiple alleles affect one and the same developmental process leading to a visible character. This effect is a graduated one for the different alleles. Take, for example, the alleles studied previously, normal and vestigial wing in Drosophila ($+^{vg}$ and vg); a considerable series of alleles exists at this locus, all of them affecting the wing in a similar but quantitatively different way. The vestigial allele (vg) removes almost all the wing blade; a more extreme allele, vg^{Nw}, removes the entire wing; a less extreme one, vg^{st}, leaves a straplike wing rudiment; a still less extreme one, vg^{no}, leaves about half of the wing blade; yet another, vg^{ni}, takes no more than small nicks from the wing. Thus we find an ascending series of mutant effects, in the order: $+^{vg} \cdots vg^{ni} \cdots vg^{no} \cdots vg^{st} \cdots vg \cdots vg^{Nw}$. In a similar way, almost all series of multiple alleles can be arranged in an ascending or descending sequence of effects. From this fact it is obvious that a series of multiple alleles must mean a series of changes in what is called a gene, altering its function in a plus or minus direction.

From the viewpoint of Mendelian genetics, multiple alleles are rather simple. Since they are merely different conditions of one and the same gene, only 1 pair of them can be present simultaneously. At the same locus on a pair of homologous chromosomes we may find, in generalized symbols, AA, aa, Aa, Aa^1, a^1a^1,

186

a^1a^2, Aa^2, etc., in other words, any pair of the existing series of multiple alleles but, of course, never more than 1 pair. Crosses between such pairs will, it is readily seen, always give simple Mendelian ratios. Just as the F_2 of $AA \times aa$ segregates into $1AA : 2Aa : 1aa$, so the F_2 of $aa \times a^1a^1$ segregates into $1aa : 2aa^1 : 1a^1a^1$. The same is true for all other possible crosses. A set of multiple alleles can therefore be recognized by its producing invariably simple Mendelian results after crossing in all possible combinations.

To grasp the full meaning of this, let us assume for a moment that a multiple allele is not a different condition of one and the same gene but a different gene located very near the other one, so that it can hardly be discriminated. If this were now the case, it would be possible to separate the 2 genes by a large-scale crossover experiment, in which there would appear a few individuals having both mutant genes in 1 chromosome and none in its partner, whereas the parents would have but 1 of the genes in each homologue. Actually, in almost all cases such an experiment gives negative results, so that multiple alleles are demonstrated to be conditions of 1 single gene.

It is interesting to inquire into the appearance, the phenotype, of the heterozygotes where multiple alleles are involved. Aa may show dominance of A or may be intermediate. In a series of multiple alleles it most frequently happens that the highest member is dominant over all the others. Thus, wild-type red eye in Drosophila is dominant over white, apricot, eosin, etc. But heterozygotes between two of the other alleles are, as a rule, intermediate.

Another problem relates to the origin of multiple allelic series by mutation. One might think that such mutants could arise in a completely haphazard way, but this is not actually the case. It is true that mutation of the wild-type allele—which we have just called the "highest" member of the series—can happen to give any other member of the series: Red eye mutates directly to white, or only to eosin, etc. Similarly, any member of the series can mutate into a lower member: Eosin may mutate to apricot or white. But a lower member hardly ever—and perhaps even never—mutates into a higher one, say white into eosin or red. If we knew the reason behind these facts, we should be able to

187

discover more about the intimate nature of the process of mutation.

Though multiple alleles are very simple as far as heredity is concerned, merely variants of the simplest kind of Mendelian heredity, they are of importance for a considerable number of problems. It is evident, for example, that the regular series of quantitatively different effects on the phenotypical expression of a trait, such as normal appearance of the fly wing blade, affords a means for finding out something about the way in which a gene controls development of a character. If all possible combinations of multiple alleles are made, if the different effects of each combination are measured, and if the development of the organ in each combination is studied, one may discover rules, relations, and regularities which permit conclusions as to the mode of gene action. Actual studies of this kind have led to very interesting results. Another problem stems from the fact that in nature multiple allelic series are sometimes found to be responsible for the variability of an organism. For instance, lady beetles are known which exhibit an enormous array of variations of pattern and color of their wings; all of these variations were shown to be based upon a single series of multiple alleles at a single locus. This genetic phenomenon thus enters into discussions of the problem of evolution. However, these and related problems are of such special and technical nature that we must here content ourselves with no more than pointing to their importance. But one case of multiple allelism has come to be of such practical importance that it must be described in greater detail. We refer to those properties of human (and other mammalian and avian) blood generally known as the blood groups, inherited conditions now widely familiar because of their importance in the correct technique of blood transfusion and in paternity tests.

The blood groups

The basis of this whole set of facts is the observation that blood has the ability to produce protective substances, so-called *antibodies,* against the harmful presence of foreign proteins, called *antigens* (which have nothing to do with the term genes). When foreign proteins enter the blood stream, as in infection or by experimental injection, these extremely important chemical

188

substances, the antibodies, are elaborated, being so constructed as to render innocuous the poisonous action of the specific foreign protein, the antigen, against which they have been formed. A special case of this general type is the presence in the red corpuscles of the blood of a special protein that, when introduced by injection into another species of animal, stimulates the production in the blood fluid of an antibody against the red corpuscles. When this blood fluid (serum) containing the specific antibodies is mixed in a test tube with the whole blood of the species against which the antibodies were formed, a reaction takes place in which the red corpuscles clump together, or are *agglutinated* (baked together).

After this phenomenon was discovered, it was found that the agglutination reaction, typical for different species, can sometimes occur when the blood of two different individuals of the same species, for example, man, is mixed. One individual's blood contained antibodies for agglutination of the other's corpuscles. Further investigation revealed that the blood of different individuals reacts in various ways, so that 4 types of people can be distinguished by the presence in their blood of an antigen called A or one called B or both together, AB, or neither antigen, the 0 group. These categories were called the blood groups. It is obvious that an individual of blood group A cannot have the antibody, now called an agglutinin, against A in his own blood, for then his own corpuscles would be agglutinated. It turned out, however, that the A individual has the agglutinin against B. Therefore, a mixture of blood from an A individual with blood from B or AB individuals results in agglutination, for the agglutinin for B present in the A blood is brought into contact with B (or AB) corpuscles. Similarly, an individual of blood group B has in his blood fluid the agglutinin against A; therefore a mixture of this fluid with A or AB blood will agglutinate the corpuscles of both. AB blood, consequently, must lack both of the agglutinins, while 0 blood contains both of them and can agglutinate the corpuscles of A, B, and AB individuals. Every person's blood group can thus be ascertained by a test-tube test, provided that the different sera are available.

Soon after all these discoveries it was recognized that comparison of the blood groups of parents and their children showed these blood types to be hereditary, based upon Mendelizing genes. These are certainly remarkable genes, controlling a trait which cannot be of any use or importance to the organism but are nevertheless present, and also have mutated, as we shall immediately see. It was quickly realized that Mendelian inheritance is involved and, after some detours into error, it turned out that the 4 blood groups are based upon a series of multiple alleles at 1 single locus of 1 chromosome. Let us express the situation in the usual genetical language, understanding that the names A, AB, B, and 0 were not intended to be Mendelian symbols but simply chanced to be chosen by the original investigator. At one point on a pair of chromosomes is located a gene that produces the effect A-type; it is dominant over a mutant that does not produce the A-type blood and is called the zero-type (0). Note that we already characterize the genes by their product, the blood type.

Had geneticists worked out the case from the beginning, they would have assigned a symbol to the gene itself, saying, for instance, that the gene *I* produces the A-type of blood and its allele *i* the 0-type. An individual of the A-type would therefore be homozygous *II* or heterozygous *Ii*. The same gene has given rise to another multiple allele, this one responsible for the B-type blood. The geneticist would have called this allele *I'*. Then an individual of blood group B could have the genotype *I'I'*, homozygous, or *I'i*, heterozygous. We know that multiple alleles may occur in a pair of chromosomes in any combination of two. Therefore an individual may have in one chromosome the allele controlling group A (we called it *I*) and in the homolologous chromosome the allele controlling group B, which was called *I'*, the genetic formula being *II'*.

Here we encounter a remarkable condition, one that is most unusual in genetics. Previously we have seen that in a pair of alleles we either have one dominant to the other or a heterozygote with a phenotype intermediate between those of the 2 homozygotes. This was also true for multiple allelic pairs. But in the heterozygote *II'* we have a quite different effect: Each of the 2 alleles produces its own characteristic effect, and there is no mixing, no interaction. The AB blood type, genetically *II'*, exhibits the proper agglutinin reactions for both the A-type and the B-type. This difference from standard Mendelian relations must be due to some unknown chemical peculiarity.

190

Finally, the 2 alleles present may be those controlling the 0-type; this individual would be genetically *ii*. A set of 3 alleles thus explains the occurrence of the 4 blood groups. In view of the confusion that may easily arise from the terminology of the blood groups, which does not follow genetical usage, the facts thus far recorded may be tabulated as follows:

Blood Group	Phenotypic Formula	Genetic Formula
A	AA or A0	II or Ii
B	BB or B0	$I'I'$ or $I'i$
AB	AB	II'
0	00	ii

It may be added that since the first discoveries other alleles have been found at the same locus, for example, the allele for a blood group B′, which we should call I^2, and which makes possible a considerable number of additional combinations of 2 alleles in any one individual. To the student of Mendelism it is clear that the results of any mating between individuals with different blood groups can be predicted as simple cases of Mendelian F_2 and backcrosses. If, for example, the mother is heterozygous for the gene controlling the A group, i.e., A0 = Ii, and the father heterozygous for the gene controlling the B group, i.e., B0 = $I'i$, the children will be expected to be one-quarter each of the types II' = AB, Ii = A0, $I'i$ = B0, ii = 0. Now one can reverse the process and draw conclusions as to the blood group of, say, the father, if the blood type of the children and mother is known. If, for example, the mother is A0 (Ii) and the child AB (II'), the father must have had B (I'), if we exclude the very rare possibility of a new mutation. The more alleles we know, the more specific can be the diagnosis. Blood group tests are therefore much used in paternity suits, and the geneticist is unable to understand why some judges still refuse to accept such evidence.

Since these primary discoveries other blood groups have been found based upon genes in other chromosomes, as is proved by their segregating separately from the first group in proper matings involving both groups. One such group is called the MN system, again with a number of multiple alleles; hence, the testing system for paternity inquiries and for transfusions has become still more refined. In the course of these studies it has also been learned that the different ethnic groups of man, the so-called races, may differ in regard to blood groups. Thus, a high frequency of 0 is found among American Indians, much A in Western Europe, much B in India. As these differences are due in part to the former history of these groups and in part to the chance preservation of mutants, it is difficult, to date, to draw many conclusions from the present distribution of blood groups. It is also of interest that the apes have the same blood groups as man. Thus the gene for the group A is to be found in the gorilla and chimpanzee.

It has already been stressed that these mutant conditions are remarkable in that they control a character which would never have become known had it not been for the serologist's experiments. It is also possible for one to think that these genes have some other effects important to the body which we have not succeeded in discovering. One additional blood group, though not different in principle from the others and, like them, based upon multiple alleles, does control certain visible effects, under certain circumstances. This is the now famous Rhesus (Rh) group.

Rhesus is the name of a species of monkey much used in laboratory experiments. If Rhesus blood is injected into a guinea pig, anti-Rhesus antibodies appear in the blood serum of the guinea pig. These anti-Rhesus substances also agglutinate some human bloods, which must therefore contain a Rhesus factor. In fact, 85% of all human beings have this factor and are for this reason said to be Rhesus positive. Only 15% are Rhesus negative. Here we have a blood factor—actually a large group of factors with small differences among them—which became known only through a complicated test. Soon after its discovery, this new blood group was found to have an extraordinary relation to a long-known pathological phenomenon. In some marriages stillbirths were known to be very frequent, or babies were born who died very soon of a mysterious condition involving destruction of blood cells. It turned out that the Rh-factor is the culprit. The child of an Rh-positive father and an Rh-negative mother will be heterozygous for this gene; further, since positive is dominant over negative, the child's blood will be positive. In the womb of the mother the child's Rhesus substances have a

192

chance to diffuse across the separating thin lining of the vessels [1] into the blood of the Rh-negative mother. If this happens— and it does happen occasionally—the mother's blood reacts by producing anti-Rhesus antibodies. These, in turn, can pass through the thin membrane of the placenta into the child's blood and there agglutinate and effectively destroy the child's corpuscles; this results sooner or later in death, either in the womb or after birth. Today every obstetrician will check upon the Rhesus groups of both parents. If the situation of positive father and negative mother exists, the mother's blood can be checked for the presence of the antibodies, and it is very often possible to save the child by proper treatment of the mother and transfusions into the child. But here we have been led far from the study of basic genetics, to which the next chapter will return.

A Glimpse of More Technical Facts
and Problems of Genetics

While studying the elementary facts of genetics we have repeatedly reached the borderline beyond which lies the more
advanced knowledge of this field. Genetics, like the other
sciences, has undergone a rapid development during the last half
century and become more and more technical. At the same time
it has reached the point where contact has been made with
physics and chemistry, so that its study requires considerable
knowledge of these fields. Other contacts have developed with
physiology, embryology, protozoology, bacteriology, and virus
research, and evolution has been emphasized even more than in
earlier years. A new upsurge of cytology, providing more intimate and intricate knowledge of the chromosomes, has posed
new problems for genetics; a special branch, cytogenetics, goes
far beyond the contents of this introduction. One might call the
whole domain beyond the elementary facts and concepts we have
studied thus far advanced genetics. Just as it is not overly difficult to explain to a beginner the essential facts of atomic structure, so the basic facts of genetics can easily be mastered. But
just as a large amount of technical knowledge is required to
achieve a detailed knowledge of the atom, with its background
of quantum theory and quantum mechanics, a study of advanced
genetics requires much technical knowledge in all the fields just
enumerated. Nevertheless, even the novice will be interested to
know where genetics stands today and what the present-day
problems are. For this reason, the present chapter will provide
a glimpse into some of the recent problems of genetics, as far
as possible without the technical preparation.

More about the study of mutation

The basis of genetical information, we have seen, is the process of mutation. The existence of what has been called a gene can be ascertained only when the gene has mutated and a cross between the mutant and the original form has revealed a pair of Mendelizing alleles. The most important properties of a gene, thus, are its ability to duplicate itself before each division of a chromosome and its ability to change by mutation into another self-duplicating mutant gene. Accordingly, the study of mutation is one of the most powerful tools for a quest into the nature of the gene. This attack can be made in different directions. An exact knowledge of natural, spontaneous mutation is required, and such information as the existence of genetic conditions within the chromosomes which influence the rate of mutation will be found to be important. Another line of attack is study of the tendency of different loci to mutate and the relation of this to location of these loci, to chromosomal structure. An important problem is whether mutations are completely haphazard, as supposed in the classical theory, or whether there is an interrelation, even a dependence, between different mutants; this is a problem which has only been touched. Another field for hopeful experimentation is provided by the existence of strains, especially of plants, in which a mutant has a tendency to mutate in the reverse direction within the cells of the individual, which thus becomes a mosaic of mutant and normal tissues. A complete understanding of this phenomenon, which is not infrequent in plants, would take us a long way towards elucidation of the process of mutation and along with it the nature of the gene.

The most popular attack upon the problem of mutation has been by the experimental production of mutants, as reported in an earlier chapter. Such experimental induction of mutations became a rather exact means for quantitative study of mutation when an ingenious method was introduced for accounting for all mutants of a particular type in one chromosome. We previously studied lethal mutants, the presence of which kills the organism at one or another stage of development. If such a lethal is located in the single X-chromosome of a male Drosophila and all would-be males in an experiment contain this lethal, no males at all will be found. The method for detecting mutants uses

195

these X-chromosome lethals; the matings, after experimental treatment of the sperm, are made in such a way that the mother also introduces a sex-linked lethal. If this test female receives, by proper matings, the experimentally treated chromosome of the male subjected to treatment, she will produce daughters only, no sons, when a sex-linked lethal mutant has originated in the treated sperm. An exact measure of one type of mutation rate is thus possible, and results obtained in different experiments can be compared. A whole science of radiation genetics has been built upon this method. This branch has also come to have some practical importance, for the sex cells of man may easily be exposed to X-rays and, eventually, the radiations produced by atomic fission, with the subsequent danger of lethal mutants in the offspring, as already mentioned above.

Chromosomal rearrangements

In the course of such experimental irradiations of chromosomes another group of facts was discovered which plays a considerable role in advanced genetics. It turned out that strong radiations, such as large doses of X-rays, as well as other treatments of chromosomes (for example, mustard gas), tend to break the chromosomes. Chromosomes have an innate tendency to unite again after breakage. However, if more than one break has been produced, reunion of the broken parts may occur in the wrong way. A smaller or larger segment may thereby be knocked out of one chromosome and either attached to another or lost completely. One chromosome in this way can become deficient. Also, a piece broken out of a chromosome may rejoin the original chromosome in the same place but with its ends in reversed positions, so that the piece is now inverted. Again, portions broken from different non-homologous chromosomes may be exchanged, so that the chromosomes come to contain segments translocated from each other. Among the many interesting features of such "deficiencies," "inversions," and "translocations" is their tendency to produce visible effects of the same type as do mutants. This gives us two major kinds of mutants: (1) those in which no change in the chromosome can be seen by our present methods, i.e., the so-called gene mutants or point mutants, which are the material of classical genetics; (2) mutants by intra- or interchromosomal rearrangement, so-called position effects. Study of

196

modes and rules according to which these two types are produced, as, say, by different radiations, promises to furnish further ideas on the nature of mutation. Some of the most searching discussions on the nature of the gene and its mutation take as their point of departure just such facts as these.

Giant chromosomes

This very elaborate branch of recent genetics has been provided with a very powerful tool by an interesting discovery, confined to the fly Drosophila and its relatives, the flies or Diptera. This instrument has extended the possibilities of relating genetic facts to chromosome structure far beyond expectation. In a number of types of cells, especially in cells of the salivary glands of the flies, the chromosomes remain visible in the resting nucleus and grow to giant size, 100 times as long as in ordinary cells. Under the microscope they exhibit a minutely fine structure: They look like long sausages with very fine cross striations that are actually caused by the alternation of stainable discs with transparent interdisc material. But the most amazing thing is that each disc—there are about 800 of them in the first chromosome—is completely constant in size, stainability, and position. Each disc can therefore be given a number and be recognized in every "salivary chromosome" from any fly (Fig. 49). One of the beautiful results is that rearrangements in the chromosomes, such as were just described, the deficiencies, inversions, and translocations, can be easily seen and the breakage points exactly localized between two definite discs. Now if we can by genetic means determine which mutant genes are located within a particular deficiency or inversion (as can be done by methods not excessively difficult), and if a sufficient number of such rearrangements are available, we can finally assign a definite location, say, within a few discs or even within a single one, to the mutant genes. The beauty of the situation is that the mapping of the salivary chromosomes by this method shows exactly the same order and arrangement of the mutants as that revealed by crossing-over experiments. And again we realize that studies of the salivary gland chromosomes coupled with genetical analysis and experimental chromosomal breakage form another avenue by which an approach to the ultimate riddles of genetics, the nature of the gene and its mutation, is possible.

197

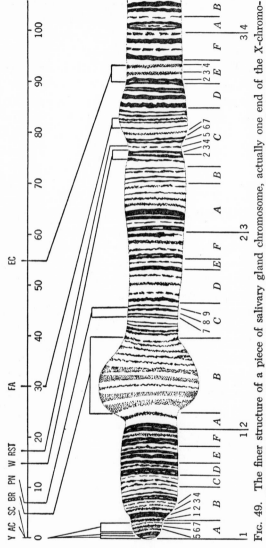

Fig. 49. The finer structure of a piece of salivary gland chromosome, actually one end of the X-chromosome of Drosophila. (*Below*) The marking system for accounting for each single band, e.g., 1, *B*, 3. (*Above*) A few mutants as arranged on a chromosome map named by their abbreviation with indication of their position in the salivary chromosome, as far as ascertained by intricate methods.

198

These giant chromosomes have opened up another line of attack. After all, the gene and the mutant gene must one day be recognized as having specific chemical, molecular constitutions. Many geneticists and biochemists are therefore actively trying to learn more about the chemical constitution of chromosomes than is contained in the statement that chromosomes consist of nucleoproteins, a combination of nucleic acids and proteins. Salivary chromosomes are large enough to be subject to all kinds of chemical and optical tests, and many facts have already been acquired which eventually may be assembled into a definitive picture of the structure of the chromosome and its component parts. In this field the chemist is in the forefront, and the geneticist eagerly awaits results that may solve his own problems.

Cytogenetics

In referring above to point mutants and mutants by rearrangement of chromosomal sections, we neglected a type of mutants already reported, those involving addition or subtraction of entire chromosomes. Earlier the giant types resulting from a doubling of all chromosomes were mentioned. This is only one type of chromosomal mutant. In plants (but hardly ever in animals) it may happen that by mutation (in this case meaning an error in chromosomal distribution in the reduction division) individuals are produced having 1 additional chromosome or 1 less than the norm. This means that one particular chromosome is present as 3 or as 1, instead of as 2. This excess or defect frequently has very definite visible effects, so that the plant appears as a mutant. The abnormality may go further. Each single chromosome of the chromosome set may occur in triplicate or only once; the visible effect in the plant will be typical and different for each particular chromosome change. It is also possible for 1 chromosome to be present 4 times, and one can easily imagine additional possibilities, some of which have been found. In plant genetics these facts are of considerable importance, and cytogenetics is especially interested in the study of them, for many details of interest to genetics, plant breeding, taxonomy, and evolution alike have been uncovered.

Cytogenetics has other problems, a few of which can merely be enumerated here. There are the details of the reduction divisions and their explanation, and the details and mechanism and more complicated consequences of crossing over form an important topic. Chromosome rearrangements lead to remarkable special features of the reduction divisions, and all kinds of abnormal behavior of the chromosomes, in turn, produce corresponding unusual types of heredity. The latter alone often gave the geneticist very hard nuts to crack, until the sometimes freakish chromosomal behavior underlying them was studied. A great field for cytogenetics is the study of the chromosomes of closely related species, leading in many cases to the disclosure of remarkable relationships, for example, differing arrangements and unions of a number of basic chromosome segments in related species having different chromosome numbers.

Genetics of lower organisms

Until recently the favorite materials of geneticists have been horticultural and agricultural plants, domestic animals, and such familiar laboratory forms as rodents, moths, and flies. In later years geneticists have climbed down the evolutionary tree to start experimenting with lower plants and animals, even down to Protozoa, fungi, algae, yeasts, bacteria, and viruses. In most of these groups—all except the bacteria and viruses—sexuality and fertilization are known, as well as typical chromosome numbers and occurrence of reduction divisions. We should therefore expect to find normal Mendelian heredity, localization of genes on definite chromosomes, crossing over, and mutation. This is indeed the case. But some additional genetic problems arise from the fact that in the lower plants the organisms have only 1 set of chromosomes through most of their life cycles and thus are comparable in this respect to the gametes of animals; and also from the fact that the reduction divisions may be connected, not with the formation of gametes, but with the production of asexual spores. Another complication is found in some Protozoa, especially in the Infusoria, where fertilization is rather different from fertilization by gametes and where other sexual processes occur in addition to the usual cytological features. But all this, though posing special problems, will not lead to genetical results which are in principle different from those of classical genetics, nor change the general statement that the hereditary

200

distribution of gene-controlled characters follows the maneuvers of the chromosomes, whatever these are in the special cases. Thus no great surprises are expected or found. These lower organisms, however, lend themselves effectively to the study of special fields of genetics, especially study of mutant changes in the biochemistry of the cell, a fact to which we shall return again.

But when we come to bacteria and viruses the surprises begin. It now looks as though bacteria have an organized nucleus and mitotic division with real chromosomes. Though there is thus far no convincing proof of a sexual cycle and fertilization in bacteria, it may be found any day. The characters, appearing as mutants, which are analyzed are either types of growth in a culture medium or the ability to use or not use specific chemicals provided by the environment. The facts discovered in the study of such mutants point to an interpretation in ordinary Mendelian terms, which would presuppose a sexual cycle with reduction division and fertilization. Genetics here is clearly ahead of cytology.

But the real surprise comes in consideration of the viruses and bacteriophages, ultramicroscopic particles having definite shapes revealed by the electron microscope. Certainly no nucleus can here be found, or any comparable structure. But again mutants are found, and their study—a rather intricate procedure—revealed facts that can best be explained in terms of Mendelian recombination and even crossing over. We must wait to see whether no other explanation can actually be found; certainly the facts are really exciting.

The cytoplasm in heredity

Classic genetics deals with the chromosomes and their content of hereditary material. But each cell consists of a nucleus, which harbors the chromosomes, and a protoplasmic cell body or "cytoplasm." The actual functions of the cell in metabolism, secretion, and differentiation must be carried out in the cytoplasm, and in one-celled organisms the cytoplasm is identical with the body of the organism. The function of the chromosomes and genes must therefore be to control in some way the activities of the cytoplasm, say by genic products, whatever these may be, entering the cytoplasm and there participating in the chemical work of the cell. The problem arises: Does the cytoplasm play any active, direct role in heredity, i.e., does such a thing as cytoplasmic inheritance exist? Geneticists have not infrequently found cases in which a difference appeared according to whether one or another genetic type was used as maternal parent, i.e., in so-called reciprocal crosses, $A \times a$ vs. $a \times A$. In such cases the phenotype of the hybrid followed the phenotype of the mother largely or exclusively. Since the mother contributed, through her egg, the cytoplasm of the embryo, the obvious conclusion was that the result may be due to a cytoplasmic influence upon heredity. Numerous experiments carried out to prove this, especially in plants and in moths, have made it certain that sometimes, but not always, the cytoplasm influences the developmental determinations controlled by a definite pair of alleles, in the heterozygote or in both homozygotes, so as to make their phenotype similar to that of the form furnishing the cytoplasm. For example:

Cytoplasm from race *AA* with genes *AA*, *Aa*, or *aa* pushes the phenotype toward that of race *AA*.

Cytoplasm from race *aa* with genes *AA*, *Aa*, or *aa* pushes the phenotype toward that of race *aa*.

We could say that in such cases the genes act differently in different cytoplasms, namely, in accordance with the way they act in the combination of a particular cytoplasm with its proper genes. But this is a long way from saying that there is a real cytoplasmic inheritance, a determination of characters by the cytoplasm alone, or, as some have put it, the existence of "cytoplasmic genes" (a bad term because the gene is defined by its location in a chromosome). For some time it looked as though some brilliant researches with Protozoa had revealed such a genuine cytoplasmic inheritance. But that interpretation turned out to be premature or, at least, oversimplified. Future positive results are not, of course, thereby excluded. In plant cells actually cytoplasmic inclusions exist (for example, the green plastids) which can change by mutation directly or under control of nuclear genes. Here are facts of great future importance, which are foremost in the minds of those interested in cytoplasmic inheritance.

202

Sex determination

In an earlier chapter we studied the determination of sex by the X-chromosome mechanism without going more deeply into the subject. Study of this phenomenon is actually one of the most fascinating though complicated problems of genetics. We studied only the mechanism which ensures that equal numbers of individuals of the sexes are produced in the normal case. But we did not try to determine how the 1X-2X mechanism actually acts to form one or the other sex. Are sex genes involved? If so, how? The general answer to this question was found in experiments on sex determination in moths and found to apply to most organisms. This answer is contained in the so-called theory of the balance of sex genes. It states that each sex has the determiners or genes for both sexes, i.e., both female and male determiners. Those of one sex, say the female sex, are located in the X-chromosome; those of the male sex, outside the X-chromosome, which may in different cases be in the autosomes, in the Y-chromosome, or in both. The male sex determiners are therefore equally present in both sexes; but the other determiners, the female ones in our example, can be present in 2 quantities (2X) or in 1 quantity (1X). If the 2 quantities of femaleness overpower the action of the male genes outside the X-chromosome, while 1 quantity of female genes in a single X-chromosome yield to the same group of male genes outside the X, then the sex chromosomes determine sex by controlling the balance between the female and male sex determiners or, more correctly, between their respective actions during sexual differentiation. An improper balance or unbalance will produce a condition intermediate between the 2 sexes called intersexuality.

Many details have been elucidated relating to the type of sex genes present or absent in X-chromosomes, Y-chromosomes, and autosomes. We already know one variant, the absence of sex genes in the Y of Drosophila. Very interesting variants are to be found in various organisms—in mammals and birds, in newts and fishes, in maize and other plants, and also in unicellular organisms. In addition, there are cases in which sex determination seems to follow another plan. And in the higher animals the hormones of the sex glands function in conjunction with the sex genes and even have a chance to change or suppress the action

203

of the sex genes. The genetics of sex is a very large field; in certain studies of it the most complicated genetical analysis known had to be made, and much of its fascination is derived from its close contact with cytology, physiology, biochemistry, embryology, and endocrinology.

The action of the genes (physiological genetics)

The preceding chapters dealt principally with the facts of hereditary transmission and the elucidation of its material basis. This is the subject matter of classical genetics. But there is another very important aspect of genetics which developed in parallel with the study of the mechanism of heredity, long remained a Cinderella, but is now becoming ready to marry the Prince Charming. The material carriers of heredity, chromosomes and genes, control, in collaboration with the cytoplasm, the development of each individual so that a given set of chromosomes and genes always produces the same result, for instance a man, a man of Mediterranean type, a Mediterranean type of tall stature, with six toes, and color blind, musical, etc. The question arises: How does the hereditary material function in development so as always to produce, under given conditions, the typical results in minutest detail? A number of roads are visible along which to attack these problems, and a branch of genetics, developmental or physiological genetics, also called phenogenetics, deals with them. Some of these lines of attack, which must be correlated with one another, are the following: The development of mutants is compared exactly with that of the normal form, and the time and nature of the divergence is determined. The same study may be combined with analysis of effects of the environment, such as different temperatures during various periods of development, in a search for definite regularities from which conclusions may be derived concerning the kinds of processes controlled by genes. These experiments can be coupled also with the use of different combinations of mutants affecting a particular organ, and a similar study of multiple alleles may uncover rules or laws. Another avenue is to study the effect of genes and their mutants in different quantities, for example, A, AA, AAA, $AAAA$, Aa, and AAa. The technique permitting such tests is mainly an outcome of experiments in which the chromosome segment containing the genes in question has been knocked out or later attached

204

to another chromosome. In these experiments on quantities one again looks for rules and regularities in the diversified actions of the genes involved; here one needs to remember the chemical principle that the masses of reacting substances are important for the process of reaction. Still another approach is to determine what sort of changes of development can be produced by experimental manipulation without genetic change. For example, when (as is actually the fact) it can be shown that the phenotypes of all well-known mutants can be reproduced or copied in the offspring of pure normals as a non-hereditary modification resulting from certain experimental treatments (so-called phenocopies), a close study of such experiments will also shed light upon the mode of action of the genes.

Biochemical genetics

Another road that has recently attained great prominence and even been found worthy of a special name, "biochemical genetics," uses genes controlling definite and definable chemical syntheses. Differences between normal and mutant phenotypes are often of a simple chemical nature. This is true for animal pigment, as in various hair colors, for the eye colors of flies, for the color of flowers; it is also true for certain chemical aberrations of metabolism resulting in production of an abnormal end product. In some of these cases, for example, flower colors, the exact chemistry of the product of the gene and its mutant types is known, so that it is possible to state that the mutant gene prevents a particular step in the synthesis of the chemical substance involved, or adds a different step to the process, or replaces one step by another. The gene thus controls a definite phase in a chemical synthesis.

The most remarkable study of this type in animals was made for the eye pigments of the flour moth and Drosophila by combining genetic data with transplantation experiments and chemical analysis. The basic plan here was to transplant a developmental stage of the eyes of particular color mutants into larvae of other mutant or wild-type forms and, on the basis of the pigment formed in the transplant, to come to conclusions concerning the substances for pigment formation in both donor and host. In a large series of difficult experiments it was possible to demonstrate that, starting with one of the (amino acid) bricks

205

of which proteins are built, the organism synthesizes the different eye pigments step by step, and that each of the known eye color genes controls one definite chemical step in the synthesis of the pigment.

A still more complete analysis became possible when a small mold, Neurospora, was used to analyze the genetic control of substances needed for growth of the organism. Numerous mutants were produced which prevented the mold from synthesizing the various amino acids and vitamins needed for protein synthesis and other processes. Further analysis by very ingenious methods revealed that for each chemical step in the synthesis of the more complicated molecules of these substances from simpler substances there could be found a gene which is assumed to control this one step of synthesis, since a mutant occurs which specifically blocks that step. In fact, this method made possible the elucidation of the course of chemical synthesis in cases in which the chemist had previously been unsuccessful. Thus a method originally devised to study the way the genes control particular chemical processes turned out to be a powerful tool for purely biochemical investigations.

Genetics and evolution

One more branch of genetics, one that has come to the fore repeatedly in earlier discussions, will be discussed: the relation of genetics to evolution. The evolution of animals and plants, in the course of the history of the earth, from simple beginnings to the highest types is a fact that no one doubts. From the viewpoint of genetics, what has occurred is an evolution of chromosomes and their genes; genetics will therefore be greatly concerned with evolutionary problems. Various lines of attack are evident, all of them in active use. The first step is to analyze genetically those differences between species and subspecies, as found in nature, that are accessible to genetic experimentation, along with cytological study, to find relations between genetic composition, distribution of organisms, and properties of the environment. Such facts will enable us to formulate conclusions as to the origin and evolution of the natural types involved.

Since evolution is the consequence of hereditary changes and since the hereditary changes so far known are mutations, this phenomenon becomes the focus of evolutionary thought. In-

206

cluded among the problems here are, of course, chromosomal mutations and also the unavoidable but still mysterious origin of those changes within chromosomes, which the geneticist would describe as the origin of new genes. The next problem is the preservation of new mutants, their ability to increase in number and eventually to replace the original form. These are the different phases and aspects of the problems of adaptation and selection. The study also includes search for the genetic basis for the survival of mutants and mutant combinations, study of competition among mutants in nature and in experimental situations, study of relationships between eventual success of mutant or mutant combination and its frequency in the population, determination of the frequency of reoccurrence of the same mutation, and investigation of migration into new environments and the effects of isolation. Attack upon all these problems involves both field and experimental work, and a subtle mathematical technique has been developed for the genetical analysis of populations. It seems hardly necessary to say that genetic analysis is possible only at the lowest taxonomic level, since even species when intermated produce, as a rule, only sterile hybrids. Many geneticists, however, think that results obtained on the subspecific level can simply be applied to all evolution and that the classic ideas of Darwin regarding evolution as the accumulation of tiny hereditary changes agree, on the whole, with recent genetic work. The future will show to what extent evolution above the lowest taxonomic level can be explained in this way.

PROBLEMS

Chapter 1

1. You find in the field many mature specimens of a plant with a great variation in size. Design an experiment to find out whether this variation is hereditary.

2. You pick from a garden 2 tobacco plants with flowers of equal size. How can you test whether they are genetically alike in regard to flower size?

3. In a species of fish you find specimens with fin rays numbering any number from 5 to 14 individually. If you study 1000 specimens, how would your result look in a graph?

4. If you shoot at a target 1000 times in succession, assuming you are a fair shot who never misses the target, how would the holes in the target be arranged?

5. Plant breeders are frequently called selectionists. (a) Why? (b) Is the name justified?

6. Will a couple of human dwarfs have dwarf children or not? Discuss the possibilities.

7. If you are told that a man who was badly burned had, afterwards, children with bluish spots of skin do you accept this as proof of inheritance of acquired characters? What investigations would you make?

Chapter 2

1. If you are told that a strong-willed man influences the *heredity* of his children more than a weakling, what would be your answer?

2. An ostrich has very large eggs, a hen smaller ones, a mammal microscopically small ones. All have sperm cells about the same small size. Does this indicate a different maternal influence upon the heredity of the offspring?

3. Man has 48 chromosomes. Is it possible that the mother contributes 20 and the father 28; or the mother 15 and the father 33, or the mother 40 and the father 8; and why or why not?

4. What would you expect to happen in the reduction division if 1 pair of homologous chromosomes did not pair but remained separate?

5. Draw a diagram of the possible arrangements of 5 pairs of chromosomes in the equatorial plate of the reduction division and the consequent

209

constitution of all sex cells in regard to chromosomes received from mother and father respectively.

6. How far back could you follow the future sex cells in the development of an animal?

7. Derive an argument against the heredity of acquired characters from the facts behind the theory of the continuity of the germ plasm.

Chapter 3

1. After crossing a red- and a white-flowered four-o'clock the hybrids are bred haphazardly for many generations. Finally you select for propagation 2 pink-flowered specimens and mate them. What will be the result?

2. In the wings of a species of moth, black is dominant over white. After breeding an F_2, you find in different experiments the following numbers: 75 black : 27 white, 82 : 19, 22 : 6, 30 : 12, 199 : 67. A foreign visitor tells you that this shows that the Mendelian ratio 3 : 1 is a figment of the imagination. What is your answer?

3. In the same cross as in Problem 2, you mate a series of pairs of black F_2 individuals. What result or results would you expect?

4. You cross a black type of a moth with a typical white one and find a simple Mendelian segregation in the F_2. Meanwhile you lost your original pure black line and you want to recover it, extract it from the F_2. Does it make a difference to your procedure and the time needed for your task whether black is completely dominant over white or whether the heterozygote is intermediate, for example, shows partly black wings?

5. You find in nature a butterfly with red wings instead of the typical yellow. You mate it with a normal yellow one. The offspring consists of 54 reds and 61 yellows. What was the genetic constitution of your original red find, and how can you prove it beyond doubt?

6. You are taken to a twin club, all members of which are twins or triplets or quadruplets. How can you find out which ones are identical?

7. Twin sisters come down with measles simultaneously. How would you proceed to prove or disprove that measles is a hereditary disease?

8. Looking at human pedigrees, what gives you the first impression that you are dealing with a dominant or a recessive trait?

Chapter 4

1. Make the following F_3 crosses with pairs taken from the F_2 Roman square, p. 80: (a) number 2 × numbers 1, 2, 3, 4, respectively; (b) number 3 × the same; (c) number 4 × the same; (d) number 6 × the same; (e) number 11 × the same; (f) number 16 × the same. Record the expected genotypes and the ratios of the phenotypes.

2. You choose at random a pair of black–short-haired guinea pigs from the F_2 in the Roman square, p. 80, and breed them until they have reared 100 young. In three such experiments, you find the following: (a) 58 black-short, 17 black-long, 20 white-short, 5 white-long; (b) 77

black-short, 23 black-long; (c) 100 black-short. What was the constitution of the parents?

3. Can the result of Problem 3c, i.e., all black-short, be explained only by one type of mating?

4. If the members of the Roman square, p. 80, were plants capable of self-fertilization instead of guinea pigs, which completely homozygous genotypes could you extract at once in the F_3 raised by selfing individual plants?

5. What types of gametes are produced by the hybrid $AaBbCcDd$?

6. Which genotypes will result from the backcross $AaBbCcDd \times aabbccdd$, and in what ratio?

7. Make a list of 10 common dominant and 10 common recessive traits in man, consulting C. Stern, *Principles of Human Genetics*, 1949, and L. H. Snyder, *Medical Genetics*, 1941.

8. In the four-o'clock, the heterozygote from the cross red flowers × white flowers is pink. Another pair of alleles is hairy vs. smooth leaves; hairy is dominant. Which phenotypes and in what ratio will be found in the F_2 from the cross red-hairy × white-smooth?

Chapter 5

1. Draw the sex cells of a hybrid between 2 organisms with a normal chromosome number of 6 and differing in 3 independent pairs of alleles $AaBbCc$. Draw the synapsis and reduction divisions of this hybrid and the resulting types of gametes.

2. Explain the terms polyhybridism, homozygous, gametes, germ track, alleles, reduction division, homologous chromosomes.

Chapter 6

1. How many groups of linked genes may be ultimately found in man?

2. In the example of black-short × white-long guinea pigs, how would the double recessive backcross be made (phenotypes and formulae)?

3. In an animal or plant you know the 6 pairs of alleles $AaBbCcDdEeFf$. You make all possible F_2 involving 2 pairs of factors, for example, $AaBb \times AaBb$. Which result will you obtain if A and B are located in chromosome I, C and F in chromosome II, D in chromosome III, and E in IV?

4. Suppose that w is the recessive white eye in Drosophila and that e is the recessive ebony color. They are located in different chromosomes. Write down the formula for the hybrid between white and ebony flies in the different notions that have been used.

5. In Drosophila, the gene v designates vermilion eyes; s, sable color; and the dominant B, bar eyes. A cross is made between $VVSSBB \times vvssbb$. The hybrid female is backcrossed to a $vvssbb$ male. The following males are obtained:

(a) vermilion–sable–normal eyes   608
(b) red (wild)–gray (wild)–Bar eyes   845

(c) red-sable-normal	97
(d) vermilion-gray-Bar	95
(e) vermilion-sable-Bar	108
(f) red-gray-normal	140

What is the order and map distance of these genes?

Chapter 7

1. How can dominant and recessive mutants in man be recognized?

2. You find a series of mutants in Drosophila which in backcrosses give you approximately the following results:

mutant a	50% wild type, 50% mutants
mutant b	60% wild type, 40% mutants
mutant c	80% wild type, 20% mutants
mutant d	99% wild type, 1% mutants
mutant e	100% wild type, ...

Which conclusions do you draw? How could you try to learn more about what is happening?

3. Curly wing in Drosophila is a dominant that is lethal when homozygous; it is located in the second chromosome. Stubble bristles show the same features, though located in the third chromosome. What is the result —phenotypes and formulae—of mating a pair of flies having both Curly and Stubble?

Chapter 8

1. In the moth Abraxas, the female is the sex with one X-chromosome (XY). A recessive gene in the X-chromosome controls a race with milk-white color of the wings. Cross (1) a milk-white female with a normal male from normal stock; (2) a normal female with a milk-white male; (3) an F_1 male from (2) with (a) a milk-white female, (b) a normal female from stock, (c) a sister female. Derive results with diagrams of sex chromosomes (L = normal, l = milk-white).

2. A color-blind man marries his cousin who is not color blind but the daughter of a color-blind father. What are the expectations for the children (boys and girls)?

3. In the diagram of the grapevine louse (Fig. 45), one kind of sperm —below left—degenerates. What would happen if by chance such sperms survived and fertilized eggs?

4. An animal known to reproduce only parthenogenetically suddenly has one or a few male offspring. For what kind of an explanation would you look?

5. In some fishes one species has XY in the female, XX in the male, and another species is XX = female, XY = male. After crossing these species, which types of offspring would you obtain in respect to the sex chromosomes?

6. In frogs, the female is XX, the male XY. It is experimentally possible to transform a female into a male without affecting the X-chromosomes. Such a transformed male is mated to a normal female. What is the sex of the offspring?

Chapter 9

1. A cross of certain strains of white sweet peas produces offspring all with purple flowers. The F_2 contains in one experiment 88 purple and 72 whites. Derive the explanation with a Roman square.

2. Make the following F_3 crosses from the F_2 mice registered in the Roman square, p. 169, and give results: (a) number 6 $\times$ number 3; (b) number 3 $\times$ number 4; (c) number 12 $\times$ number 16; (d) number 4 $\times$ number 16; (e) number 3 $\times$ number 14.

3. Mate a black piebald mouse with albino number 6 of the foregoing Roman square. What is the phenotype of the offspring?

4. There is a dominant gene in fowl producing a double comb, genetically independent of rose or pea comb. You cross double comb with pea comb and call this F_1 number 1. You further cross rose comb $\times$ double comb and call this F_1 number 2. Now you mate F_1 number 1 $\times$ F_1 number 2. Make a Roman square and state phenotypes and ratios.

Chapter 10

1. A plant homozygous for a character, like shape of leaf, is selfed. Nevertheless in the offspring, the character shows considerable variation. There are two possible explanations. What are they? How can you prove either?

2. In the early days of genetics it was claimed that a cross between short- and long-eared rabbits was intermediate and that this intermediate condition remained in the following generations (so-called blending inheritance). What error was committed?

3. You are told that a mulatto—F_1 between Negro and white—married a white woman and among their children was a very dark black one. What does the geneticist answer?

4. You are told that a shepherd dog was mated to a poodle and produced some litters of mongrels. Afterwards she was mated to a pure shepherd male. In her litter some poodle mongrels are said to have appeared. What is your answer?

5. You cross 2 plant lines showing great quantitative differences, for example, much oil in the seed vs. hardly any. In the F_2, you get some oily seeds but far less oily than the original parents. You breed the F_3 from the oiliest F_2 seeds and again the original standard of oiliness is not recovered. The same happens in F_4: You get oily seeds and still not so oily as the original. If oil content is completely controlled by the genetic constitution, what conclusions do you draw regarding the genetic basis of high oil content and why?

Chapter 11

1. White, cream, cherry, apricot, and eosin eye color in Drosophila are multiple alleles (recessive). Cross a white fly with a cherry one, the F_1 female (because these genes are sex-linked) with an apricot male, and all the resulting types of F_2 females with eosin males. What is the phenotype and genetic constitution of this F_3 (females and males)?

2. A purple-eyed fly is crossed with a cherry-colored one. In the F_2 red, purple, cherry, and a new combination color appear. Is this a case of multiple alleles? Why or why not?

3. In a paternity suit a mother has the blood type AB and the child is A. Can a man with AB have been the father?

4. A man of blood group B is accused of having fathered a child having type 0. The mother turns out to be type A. Can he be the father? Must he be the father?

Chapter 12

Look up in the library all available texts on genetics (for example, Sinnott-Dunn, Shull, Altenburg, Colin, Snyder) and find out which one contains the most elaborate discussion on each of the advanced subjects mentioned in this chapter.

Books for Further Study

1. Popular and semipopular:

Boyd, W. C. (1950), Genetics and the Races of Man. Little, Brown & Co., Boston.

Dunn, L. C., and Th. Dobzhansky (1946), Heredity, Race and Society. Pelican Books, Penguin Books, New York.

Scheinfeld, A. (1950), The New You and Heredity. J. B. Lippincott, Philadelphia.

Winchester, A. M. (1951), Genetics: A Survey of the Principles of Heredity. Houghton Mifflin Co., Boston.

2. Standard college texts of different scope, size, and technicality arranged in the order of increasing technicality:

Colin, E. C. (1946), Elements of Genetics. Blakiston Co., Toronto.

Riley, H. P. (1948), An Introduction to Genetics and Cytogenetics. John Wiley & Sons, New York.

Shull, A. F. (1948), Heredity. 4th edition. McGraw-Hill, New York.

Snyder, G. H. (1951), The Principles of Heredity. 3rd edition. D. C. Heath, New York.

Altenburg, E. (1945), Genetics. Henry Holt, New York.

Sinnott, E. W., L. C. Dunn, and Th. Dobzhansky (1951), Principles of Genetics. 4th edition. McGraw-Hill, New York.

Sturtevant, A. H., and G. W. Beadle (1939), An Introduction to Genetics. W. B. Saunders, Philadelphia.

3. Advanced and less advanced books covering special chapters of genetics like cytology, cytogenetics, evolution, sex determination, and general genetics—books not meant as college texts of genetics:

Darlington, C. D., and K. Mather (1949), The Elements of Genetics. The Macmillan Company, New York.

Dobzhansky, Th. (1951), Genetics and the Origin of Species. 3rd edition. Columbia University Press, New York.

Goldschmidt, R. B. (1923), The Mechanism and Physiology of Sex Determination. Methuen & Co., London.

215

Goldschmidt, R. B. (1938), Physiological Genetics. McGraw-Hill, New York.

Goldschmidt, R. B. (1940), The Material Basis of Evolution. Yale University Press, New Haven.

Huxley, F. S. (1942), Evolution, The Modern Synthesis. Harper and Brothers, New York.

Mayr, E. (1942), Systematics and the Origin of Species. Columbia University Press, New York.

Sharp, L. W. (1944), Introduction to Cytology. 2nd edition. McGraw-Hill, New York.

Shull, A. F. (1951), Evolution. 2nd edition. McGraw-Hill, New York.

Simpson, G. G. (1945), Tempo and Mode in Evolution. Columbia University Press, New York.

Stebbins, G. L. (1951), Variation and Evolution in Plants. Columbia University Press, New York.

Stern, C. (1950), Principles of Human Genetics. W. H. Freeman, San Francisco.

Waddington, C. H. (1939), An Introduction to Modern Genetics. The Macmillan Company, New York.

White, M. J. D. (1945), Animal Cytology and Evolution. Cambridge University Press, Cambridge.

Glossary

ACQUIRED CHARACTER. A property of the organism acquired during life as a consequence of actions of the external or internal environment.

AGGLUTINATION. The baking together of small particles, especially red blood corpuscles, produced in different ways.

ANTIBODY. Chemical substance produced in the blood to neutralize the action of foreign protein.

ANTIGEN. Substance which if introduced into a foreign body causes the production of specific antibodies.

ALLELES (al le'les) (Greek *allelos,* one or the other). A pair of Mendelian genes at the same locus of a pair of homologous chromosomes.

ALLELIC (al le'lic). Acting as a pair of alleles.

ASEXUAL REPRODUCTION. Reproduction without sex cells, by division, budding, or cuttings.

ATAVISM (Latin *atavus,* ancestor). The appearance of ancestral traits.

BACKCROSS. The cross of a hybrid with one of its parental forms.

BACTERIOPHAGE. A virus-like submicroscopic organism which attacks and destroys bacteria.

BREEDING TRUE. Producing identical offspring over all generations because of homozygosity.

BUD VARIATION. A mutant of body cells affecting only a part of a plant, e.g., a bud.

CHROMATIN (chro'ma tin) (Greek *chromos,* color). The substance in the chromosomes which stains with certain basic dyes (because of the presence of nucleic acids).

CHROMOSOME MAP. A diagrammatic map representing the location of genes on the chromosomes.

CHROMOSOME NUMBER. The number of paired chromosomes typical for any species.

CHROMOSOMES (chro'mo somes) (Greek *chromos,* color; *soma,* body). The specific chromatic bodies visible during division of the nucleus.

CONTINUITY OF THE GERM PLASM. The generalization from the fact of direct derivation of sex cells from the substance of the maternal sex cell (the egg of the mother).

CROSS. A mating between two genetically differing individuals.

CROSSING OVER. The exchange of chromosomal segments between homologous chromosomes.

217

CROSSOVER FREQUENCY. The typical percentage in which exchange between a pair of loci in the same chromosome occurs (frequency of breaks between two loci).

CURVE OF CHANCE. The symmetrical curve (binomial in the ideal case) of frequencies of events or structures which vary under the impact of the environment, i.e., by action of chance.

CYTOGENETICS (cy'to ge net'ics) (Greek *kyton*, cell). The science of the cell.

CYTOPLASM (cy'to plasm) (Greek *kyton*, cell; *plasma*, formative substance). The protoplasmatic body of the cell and its extranuclear inclusions.

DEFICIENCY. The absence of a section of a chromosome.

DIHYBRID. A hybrid for two pairs of Mendelizing alleles.

DOMINANCE (Latin *dominare*, rule). The phenotypic suppression of the visible action of one of a pair of alleles by the other.

DOMESTICATION. The taming and breeding of originally wild animals by man.

DOUBLE RECESSIVE BACKCROSS. Backcross of a hybrid involving two pairs of alleles with the double recessive parental form.

DROSOPHILA. Banana fly, vinegar fly, or fruit fly.

ENDOCRINOLOGY. The science of internal secretions or hormones.

EPISTASIS (Greek *epi*, above; *stasis*, standing). The suppression of the visible action of one gene by one not its allele.

EVOLUTION. The fact that animals and plants have originated by slow transformation from simple to more advanced forms.

EXTRACT. To pick out and propagate Mendelian segregants after crossing.

FERTILIZATION. The union of egg and sperm (pollen), especially the union of maternal and paternal nuclei.

GAMETES (gam'etes) (Greek *gamein*, mate). The sex cells of either sex.

GENE. The smallest section of a chromosome separable from another one by crossing over, and considered the unit of heredity.

GENETIC (ge net'ic). Controlled by heredity.

GENOTYPE (gen'o type). The genetic constitution of an organism independent of the visible appearance.

GERMPLASM. The sum total of the genes (plus eventual other determiners of heredity) of an organism.

HETEROZYGOTE (het'er o zy'gote) (Greek *heteros*, the other; *zygotos*, united). An organism containing for a given locus a pair of different alleles (or for more than one locus).

HETEROZYGOUS. The condition of having a pair of different alleles.

HEMOPHILIA (Greek *haimos*, blood; *philos*, friend). The bleeder's disease.

HOMOLOGOUS CHROMOSOMES. The two members of one pair of chromosomes, one of maternal, one of paternal, origin.

HOMOZYGOTE (ho'mo zy'gote) (Greek *homos*, alike; *zygotos*, united). An individual with two identical genes at one (or more) loci of a chromosome.

HOMOZYGOUS. The condition of the presence of identical genes at one (or more) loci.

218

HYBRID (Greek *hybris,* crime). The offspring of two in any way genetically different parents.

HYBRIDIZE. The crossing to produce a hybrid.

IDENTICAL TWINS. Twins developed from a single egg.

INDIVIDUALITY OF THE CHROMOSOMES. The unaltered retention of the genetic texture as well as the visible features of all chromosomes through the cell generations and generations of individuals (if no mutation occurs).

INTERSEXUALITY. A condition, in between the two sexes, produced by genetic or hormonic abnormalities.

INVERSION. The breakage of a chromosome at 2 points, followed by reinsertion of the broken-out piece after turning 180 degrees.

ISOAGGLUTININS. Antibodies produced against antigens within the same species, e.g., the blood groups.

LETHAL GENE (Latin *letalis,* fatal). A mutant gene, the effects of which destroy the developing organism at any stage from egg to adult.

LINKAGE. The genetic association of two genes which act as if inseparable, usually because they are located on the same chromosome. The linkage is broken by crossing over.

LOCUS (Latin *locus,* place). A small section of a chromosome at a definable point. In practice locus may mean the place of location of a gene or the gene itself.

MAP DISTANCE. The distance between two genes on a chromosome as measured in percentage of crossing over.

MENDELIAN RATIO. The ratio of phenotypes in a sibship with Mendelian segregation.

MENDELISM. The science of heredity according to Mendel's scheme.

MENDELIZE. Behaving according to the rules of Mendelian heredity.

MITOTIC DIVISION (Greek *mitos,* thread). Cell division involving chromosomes and threadlike plasmatic structures.

MODIFIERS. Genes which affect the phenotype controlled by one or more pairs of mutant genes.

MULTIPLE ALLELES. A series of 3 or more alleles of one and the same gene.

MULTIPLE FACTORS. Series of different genes affecting the same phenotypic character, usually in a quantitative (additive or multiplicative) way; also called polygenes.

MUTANT. An individual in which at least one locus has changed by mutation (gene mutant), or in which have occurred changes by rearrangement within or doubling, etc., of one to all chromosomes.

MUTATIONS. The changes in genes or chromosomes which produce mutants.

NICHE (French, a nook). Locality endowed with special environmental conditions (example: alpine habitat); also a set of environmental peculiarities without separate locality (examples: air, or water, or all flowers with nectar).

OVARY. Female sex glands in plants and animals.

PARTHENOGENESIS (par'the no gen'e sis) (Greek *parthenos,* virgin; *genesis,* origin). Virginal reproduction, i.e., without fertilization.

PHENOCOPY. Non-hereditary variant indistinguishable visibly from a hereditary mutant.

219

PHENOTYPE (Greek *phainein,* appear). The visible type, whether based upon heredity or not.

PHYLLOXERA (phyl lox'era). The aphid of the grapevine.

PLASTIDS (Greek *plaston,* the formed thing). Bodies in the cytoplasm of plant cells containing the chlorophyll, etc., and partly controlled by the cell, partly endowed with independent behavior.

POLAR BODIES. The small and doomed cells produced by the maturation division of the egg cell.

POLYDACTYLY (pol y dac'ty ly) (Greek *polys,* many; *daktylos,* finger). The hereditary presence of more than five fingers (or toes) in different animals and man.

POLYGENES (pol'y gene). *See* Multiple factors.

POLYHYBRID (pol'y hy'brid) (Greek *polys,* many). A hybrid heterozygous for a number of genes.

POPULATION. A large number of individuals chosen at random, or all of a given group.

PREADAPTATION. A mutational change in one or more genes carried in a population, which enables their bearer to fill a new niche of environment if chance presents itself.

PROGENY TEST. Testing the genetic constitution of an organism by breeding further generations.

PURE LINE. Offspring of one self-fertilizing individual continuing the procedure over many generations.

PURE RACE. A breeding group, homozygous for all genes under consideration.

PURITY OF GAMETES. The fact that gametes of hybrids are pure for one or the other of a pair of alleles.

RECESSIVE (Latin *recedere,* to yield). The allele which in the heterozygote does not produce a visible effect.

REDUCTION DIVISION. The division(s) in the maturation of the sex cells which separates whole chromosomes, thus reducing the normal number of chromosomes to half that number.

RECOMBINATION (Mendelian). The different combinations of 2 or more pairs of alleles in F_2 of a cross.

ROMAN SQUARE. Simple method of writing chance combinations, e.g., between two sets of gametes.

SEGREGATION (Mendelian). The splitting of F_2, etc., into different types, based upon reshuffling of parental genes in the maturation divisions of the hybrid.

SELECTION. Generally, choosing individuals for propagation; specifically, making such a choice in order to breed definite types. Natural selection means the same kind of choice occurring in nature because of superiority of one or many genetic constitutions in the struggle for survival.

SEX CELLS. Eggs and spermatozoa.

SEX CHROMOSOMES. The chromosome pairs which show specific features responsible for the mechanism of distribution of offspring between the two sexes (*X*- and *Y*-chromosomes).

SEX-LINKED INHERITANCE. The type of heredity resulting from the location of a gene in a sex chromosome.

SOMA (so'ma) (Greek, body). The body and its cells, as opposed to the sex cells.

SOMATIC CELLS (so mat'ic cells). All cells except the sex cells.

SPERMATOZOON (sper'ma to zo'on) (plural *zoa*) (Greek *sperma,* sperm; *zoon,* living being). The male sex cells.

SPORT. Old breeders' term for mutant.

SYNAPSIS (syn ap'sis) (Greek *syn,* together; *haptein,* stick). The pairing point by point of homologous chromosomes before the maturation division of the gametes.

TAXONOMY (tax on'o my). The science which describes and catalogues the forms of animals and plants (also called systematics).

TESTIS. Male sex gland.

TETRAHYBRID (tet'ra hy'brid) (Greek *tetra,* four). A heterozygote in 4 pairs of genes.

TRIHYBRID. A heterozygote in 3 pairs of genes.

TRANSLOCATION. The insertion of a part of a chromosome (or the whole) into another, not homologous, chromosome, reciprocally or not.

VIRUS. Submicroscopic body which can live only together with other organisms and shows essentially the features of Mendelian heredity in the proper setup. Some appear to be pure nucleoprotein.

Index

Acquired characters, 24, 25, 27
Agglutination, 188 ff.
Alleles, and chromosomes, 104
 definition, 65
 multiple, 185 ff.
 numbers of pairs, 105
Animal husbandry, 89, 142
Antibodies, 188 ff.
Antigen, 188 ff.
Asexual reproduction, 51, 52
Atavism, 164 ff.
Autosomes, 146, 153, 203

Bacterial heredity, 194, 200, 201
Bacteriophage, 201
Beans, environmental effects, 12, 13,
 14, 16
 mixed strains, 15 ff.
 progeny tests, 12, 13
 pure lines, 180
 selection, 15, 16, 17
 variation, 7, 12, 13, 16, 17
Biochemical genetics, 205 ff.
Bleeder's disease, see Hemophilia
Blood groups, 188 ff.
 ABO group, 190
 distribution in races, 192
 heredity, 190 ff.
 in mammals and birds, 192
 MN group, 191
 multiple alleles, 190 ff.
 paternity tests, 191
 Rhesus group, 192 ff.
Brachydactyly, 76, 143
Bud variation, see Mutation

Cats, 25
Cell division, 30, 93

Cell theory, 28
Centrosomes, 31
Chance, laws of, 17
Chiasma, 123
Chromatin, 30
Chromosome maps, 127, 128, 129,
 197
Chromosomes, 30
 addition and subtraction, 199
 autosomes, 146, 153, 203
 breakage, 123, 197, 199
 chiasmata, 123
 deficiency, 196, 197
 in dihybridism, 98 ff.
 division, 32, 33
 doubling, 199
 of Drosophila, 197
 and evolution, 199
 in fertilization, 37, 38, 39, 40
 and genes, 94 ff., 98, 105
 giant, 197
 homologous, 45, 94, 96, 104
 individuality, 45, 50
 inversion, 196, 197
 loci, 97 ff.
 in maize, 112, 128, 129
 in man, 31, 50, 104, 105, 112, 129
 mapping of, 125 ff., 129
 and Mendelism, 93 ff.
 numbers, 31, 94
 in Phylloxera, 150 ff.
 rearrangements, 196
 reduction, 41, 43 ff., 46, 47, 94
 salivary gland, 197
 and sex, 144 ff., 203 ff.
 size of, 39
 of snapdragon, 112, 129
 synapsis, 96, 100

223

225

227